Pamela Buchanan was born in Lake Forest, Illinois, educated in France, England, and Switzerland, and lives in the South of France. She serves as emeritus trustee on the boards of the Buchanan Foundation of Chicago; the James Gatz Charitable Trust in Bismarck, North Dakota, and the Carraway Institute of St. Paul, Minnesota; all three of which she founded. Her previous books include: *American Countess*, an account of her first marriage, and *Married to Figaro*, an account of her second.

For my mother.

Pamela Buchanan

DAISY

AUSTIN MACAULEY PUBLISHERS™

LONDON • CAMBRIDGE • NEW YORK • SHARJAH

Ordering Information
Quantity sales: Special discounts are available on quantity purchases by corporations, associations, and others. For details, contact the publisher at the address below.

Publisher's Cataloging-in-Publication data
Buchanan, Pamela
Daisy

ISBN 9781685623029 (Paperback)
ISBN 9781685623036 (Hardback)
ISBN 9781685623043 (ePub e-book)

Library of Congress Control Number: 2023904728

www.austinmacauley.com/us

First Published 2023
Austin Macauley Publishers LLC
40 Wall Street, 33rd Floor, Suite 3302
New York, NY 10005
USA

mail-usa@austinmacauley.com
+1 (646) 5125767

Although this is a work of fiction, I would like to acknowledge the following non-fiction books that helped in our research:

Living Well is the Best Revenge, by Calvin Tomkins
Everybody Was So Young, by Amanda Vaill
Hotel Florida, by Amanda Vaill
Sara and Gerald, by Honorie Murphy
We Saw Spain Die, by Paul Preston
The Spanish Civil War, by Hugh Thomas
The Spanish Civil War, by Anthony Beevor
Spain in Our Hearts. By Adam Hochschild
The Breaking Point, by Stephen Koch
The Windsor Years, by Lord Kinross

Table of Contents

Preface

There can be no doubt that my mother had many lovers; my father, too, but his tended to be chambermaids and floozies, far less interesting than my mother's liaisons. From the vantage point of extreme old age, I can look back on all this now with a certain detachment. Everybody involved in this story is long dead and gone, and I will be joining them soon enough. The times in which they and I lived are as remote and disembodied from the present as the sound of a gramophone on a soft summer night playing:

I'm the Sheik of Araby,
Your love belongs to me.
At night when you're asleep
Into your tent I'll creep.

That was one of my mother's favorites when she and her century were in their early twenties. As a young girl, I adored my father with his straw-blond hair, his broad shoulders and gruff manner, but in the many decades of research I have put into these rambling accounts, I have come to realize that he was not what you would call a nice man. There were men on two continents who hated his guts.

But he had a kind of animal magnetism that pulled some people to him.

What follows here, however, is about my mother, Daisy, who had her moments of weakness, but who possessed a certain style nonetheless, and in an odd way a kind of doughty courage that made up for her frivolities. Men found her attractive, with her shining hair and lively eyes. My uncle Nick used to say that she had a low, thrilling voice that seemed to promise she had done gay, exciting things, and that there would be gay exciting things in the next hour. But he also said of my parents that they were careless people who smashed up things and then retreated into their vast carelessness and let other people clean up the messes they had made.

Nick Carraway wasn't really my uncle. He was my mother's second or third cousin two or three times removed, but there were times when he was all the family I had. I was always glad for his letters when I was young and being brought up by nannies or warehoused in boarding schools, as was the custom of the American rich in those days, perhaps aping the British. Uncle Nick was the only one who ever came to see me at my school on the shores of Lake Geneva. But then few of the girls ever had family visitors. That was the whole point. Parents knew we were safe, and they were paying a good deal of money so they didn't have to bother with us.

Uncle Nick had been a classmate of my father's at Yale, and a club mate at Skull and Bones, the secret society in which between the chosen there are supposed to be no secrets. I still have the gold death's head pin with the crossed femurs that my father kept in a little leather box along with his cufflinks and shirt studs. Uncle Nick was very helpful to me when I began this quest for knowledge about my mother so many years ago. Why would I spend so much time and money on such a quest, you may ask. And indeed, I have asked myself the same question. I never really knew my mother. She was just a glamorous woman I called Mummy, who might give me a fleeting kiss as she was dressing for dinner before handing me back to Nanny.

As I noted, this is not a story about me, so I will introduce myself quickly and then step away. I was an only child. My mother was disappointed when I was born. She wanted a son. She said she hoped I would grow up to be a 'beautiful little fool'. As it turned out I was certainly not the former, and I hope not the latter. I have degrees from Oxford and the Sorbonne. I speak four languages fluently and am conversant in two more. Although I was considered pretty when I was very little, in my teens my face coarsened and took on the heavy look of my father, and my body soon followed suit. Unlike either of my parents, I was awkward and clumsy. My eyesight has never been good, and the glasses designed by my optician, Dr. Eckleburg, made me look owlish.

A series of Scottish nannies and interchangeable French governesses named Mademoiselle formed the basis of my childhood. I was married twice, once to a Frenchman whom I loved, and then to an Argentine adventurer whom I did not. I guess you could say they both married me for my considerable fortune. For a time, I was referred to as a countess in certain circles, and still could be if I chose. But I have long since reverted to my maiden name, which is less confusing for the bankers who oversee my trust funds and charities in New York, London, Chicago, and Geneva.

My first husband died at the wheel of his beloved Lancia at the stroke of midnight on the Moyenne Corniche between Nice and Monte Carlo. The girl he was with was paralyzed in the crash, and somehow because I had given him the car, I was expected to pay for her care for the rest of her life. My second husband cost me a great deal of money to divorce. I would not say I have lived an interesting life, but my foundations and the many boards I have been asked to join have kept me useful. My quest for information about my parents, you could say, has kept me busy.

Now that I have reached my one hundredth year, I have become something of a recluse, living an expatriate life in the company of loyal Spanish servants in my fading villa now ravaged by old age, much like myself. Most of my former neighbors are no longer with us, including my old friend, Willie Maugham, with whom I used to play bridge twice a week. But the view through the alley of Cypress trees to the Bay of Villefranche is as enchanting as I first saw it so many years ago. I have traveled far to talk with those who knew my mother, and some who loved her. Those interviews and her diaries, notes and letters have given me an outline of her life. There is more to do, perhaps in Moscow, but my health is fading now, and I have neither the time nor the inclination to dig for more. So, with the help of my old friend and confidant, David (HDS) Greenway, whom I have known for sixty-five years, here is what I know about my mother, Daisy.

Pamela Buchanan

Cap Ferrat, France, 2021

Chapter 1

My mother, Daisy Anne Scott Fay, was born in the last year of the 19th century in Louisville, Kentucky. The Anne Scott was for the first Duchess of Buccleuch, from whom the Fays and Uncle Nick believed we were descended. The Duke of Buccleuch never recognized that relationship, which caused my mother some embarrassment when my father tried to claim it; but I am getting ahead of my story. The Fays lived on a leafy street in one of the largest houses in Louisville. They had plenty of money, although not on the scale of my father's family. The Fays were of Anglo-Irish stock, having arrived in Virginia in the seventh decade of the 17th century. They were among Kentucky's earliest settlers, having moved west in 1779 into what was then Kentucky County, Virginia, before Kentucky became a state of its own.

My great grandfather Fay served in the Confederate Army even though his native state opted to stay with the Union. President Lincoln was wont to say he would be happy to have God on his side, but he *must* have Kentucky. In the end, he had Kentucky, but not Jeremiah Fay, whose gloomy opinion of the times in which he lived justified his

Christian name. It was in his nature to side with Jefferson Davis rather than the Great Emancipator.

Daisy was by far the most popular girl in town—the 'it girl', as we used to say—and with her bobbed hair, her charming pout, and her low, exhilarating ripple of a voice, she was nothing less than enchanting. She spoke so softly that people had to lean forward to hear her words, which was of course part of her charm. She cut a dashing figure driving in her white Dodge Brothers roadster. Automobiles were not that common in 1917. The Dodge Brothers had only been in business four years, and only a few young people had an automobile of any marque. Daisy was surrounded by would-be swains, of course, and with her signature stutter she used to say things such as, "I'm p-paralyzed with happiness," as if, as Uncle Nick used to say, "Her whole heart was trying to come out to you concealed in one of those breathless, thrilling words." She had that great knack of making every young man she was with think that he was the only one she wanted to be with.

When she was eighteen, she fell in love with an elegant young ruffian from North Dakota who was training in nearby Camp Taylor for the Great War, which America had just joined. For him, Daisy's musical voice chimed with all the money he did not have. For him, she was his incorruptible dream. Her parents deeply disapproved, of course. He was of dubious background, and they were sure he played on her heartstrings with romantic notions of his going off to fight the Hun, perhaps never to return. The family found out later that his name was James Gatz, but that was not the name he used when he was courting Daisy. Then he called himself Jay Gatsby, which made him sound more patrician. It is likely that Daisy had her first sexual experience with Gatz on a still October night, for she moped a good deal after he had gone to war.

But by the autumn of 1918, she was her old self again and had her debut, or coming out party, as they say nowadays, right after the Armistice. Les tout Louisville showed up, and the old photographs show Daisy in the role of the virginal Southern belle again. She was soon engaged to a limp young man from New Orleans, what we used to call a tall drink of water. He had come especially for her debut and hung around afterward to be near her. But that brief romance didn't survive Daisy's meeting my father when he came for another Louisville party. After the briefest of courtships, Thomas Macpherson Buchanan and Daisy were married that June. I came along the following April.

My father's grandfather Angus Buchanan arrived penniless from Scotland before the Civil War and built up a dry grocery business in the burgeoning Midwest, eventually making a fortune mining in Minnesota, as well as railroading and shipping, too. He was instrumental in opening the Northwest, along with the Canadian-born railroad man, James Hill. It is said that when their train was halted in a snowstorm one night, Hill and Buchanan dismounted from their private cars and, in their fur-collared greatcoats and yellow pigskin gloves, grabbed shovels and helped the railroad workers clear the tracks. Old Angus benefited financially from the showdown between Hill and Harriman over control of the Northern Pacific in 1901 and died one of the richest men in Chicago.

His grandson, Tom, went to Phillips Academy in Andover, Massachusetts, where he excelled at sports, and then Yale, where he became a celebrated football player in an era when football at Yale was of national renown. Uncle Nick used to say that Tom was so good at that sport that everything else in his later life was an anticlimax. To the end of his life, he always seemed to be "seeking the dramatic turbulence of some irrecoverable football game," Uncle Nick would say. He also became a famous polo player, one of the few undergraduates to have his own string of polo ponies in New Haven.

Attempting to understand my father, I engineered a clandestine visit to Skull and Bones many years ago. I had met a young Rhodes Scholar at Oxford, a soon-to-be doctor and Bones man who while drinking used to regale us with indiscreet stories about his days at Yale. When back in America, in a moment of supreme indiscretion, he let me in late one night to visit the society's gloom-filled building, rightfully called a tomb, which had counted three American presidents and countless other members of the American establishment among its brotherhood. I had taken the train up from New York during one of my frequent visits to America for no other purpose but this. The young man has long since died, and I feel it is no longer breaking my vow of silence on the matter. To assuage his guilt I arranged for the Buchanan Foundation to finance his cancer research projects for many years.

My most vivid memory of Skull and Bones is a picture of a burial vault with four skulls. The caption reads: *Wer war der Thor, wer Weiser, wer Bettler oder Kaiser?* "Who was the fool, who the wise man, beggar or king?" The place reeked of 19th century German romanticism, which may or may not have contributed to my father's pessimistic view of life. But despite this egalitarian message, it was clear that my father's athletic prowess, his Bones membership, and his money gave him an exaggerated sense of entitlement that never left him. This was never true of Uncle Nick, who, I am happy to say, never knew about my clandestine visit.

The Buchanans made a great impression on Louisville society when they came down from Lake Forest in four private railway cars with a wedding party of almost one hundred people, hiring several floors of the Seelbach Hotel. My godmother, Jordan Baker, one of the most famous female golfers of her time, told me years after that Daisy nearly called off the wedding in a fit of nerves and second thoughts. But she pulled herself together, and the ceremony at the Highland Presbyterian Church went off without anyone's knowing of Daisy's doubts. The honeymoon couple sailed in and around Tahitian waters in the Buchanans' yacht for three months with a crew of twelve in the days when natives still remembered that old reprobate Paul Gauguin.

Of course, I had to see for myself where Daisy and Tom had been happy, and the Belgian singer Jacques Brel was kind enough to fly me in his twin-engined Dassault to the islands where my parents had sailed. It was Brel's habit to fly sick Polynesians in the out-islands to hospital in Tahiti, and because he was having trouble with the Dassault, I promised to buy him a new plane. But he was mortally ill at the time and died before I could fulfill my promise. To this day I pay for the upkeep of his grave on a beautiful hillside overlooking Atuona Bay on the island of Hiva Oa, a few meters away from Gauguin's grave. As far as gaining insights into my parents' lives, however, my trip to French Polynesia was a failure.

From all accounts, Daisy was deliriously happy in the first few months of matrimony. But soon after they returned to America, her new husband's peccadilloes began casting clouds over their marriage. There was a chambermaid in Santa Barbara who had to be hushed up and paid off. Daisy and Tom went to live in France for a summer, and there was a young belle poule in a Normandy hotel whom Daisy mentioned fleetingly in tear-stained letters to Aunt Jordan. There was an incident back in Chicago, too, a scandal that sent them scuttling to the East Coast. Aunt Jordan said it had something to do with the wife of one of their servants, but she wasn't sure of the details.

As far as I can piece it together, the most serious scandal came in the summer of 1922. We were living on the North Shore of Long Island, in a big house on the sound, when Daisy's old flame James Gatz showed up again. Being a toddler at the time, I have no memory of him. It seems he had returned from the war a hero, having wiped out a German machine gun company or something equally unpleasant. He gave my mother a medal he had won for 'extraordinary valor', the *Orderi di Danilo* from King Nicholas of Montenegro. He had become very rich—no one knew just how—and he gave fabulous parties in a Loire-style chateau even bigger than our Italianate house across the bay, parties that in some ways defined that frivolous decade of declining morals and bootleg gin: The twenties. He was still living under his assumed name. In America, it has always been possible to reinvent yourself, to become

20

something you wish to be, rather than what you are, and that became Gatz's overwhelming self-absorption.

It came out later that Gatz had gotten involved with the bootlegger Meyer Wolfsheim; both making a great deal of money buying drugstores so that they could buy and sell alcohol openly in those Prohibition days. Wolfsheim became famous for fixing the World Series in 1919, having allegedly bribed Shoeless Joe Jackson, Lefty Williams, Chick Gandil, and four others of the Chicago White Sox to throw the games so that the Cincinnati Reds could win.

Apparently Gatz had bought his house on the North Shore in the hopes that Daisy might come to one of his parties, even though he never formally invited the Buchanans. He just hoped that someone else would bring them, or that they might show up uninvited, as so many others did. When Daisy never came, it fell to Uncle Nick, who by chance had rented a small house next to Gatz, to arrange a meeting.

Nick invited his cousin for tea, and they arranged that Gatz would drop by as if by chance. Given how that summer ended, it is no wonder that Uncle Nick felt guilty for the rest of his life that he had been party to that subterfuge. Gatz, hopeful of resuming their old relationship, asked Daisy to leave my father and run away with him. Daisy, flustered and flirtatious, and not a little angry at her husband's love affairs, toyed with the idea.

Then one hot summer afternoon, Daisy, my father, Uncle Nick, and Aunt Jordan drove with Gatz in two cars into New York to the Plaza Hotel. There was some kind of altercation between Gatz and my father over which one Daisy really loved. Father made fun of Gatz's British affectations. Gatz used to call people 'old sport' in a stilted manner that was just short of being absurd. My mother and Gatz left together to drive back to Long Island with Daisy at the wheel in my father's car. The others followed on a bit later. By a horrible coincidence, a woman, the wife of a garage mechanic, with whom my father was having an affair, rushed out in the road trying to flag down what she had recognized as Tom's car. Daisy wasn't quick enough to swerve, and the fender caught the woman and killed her instantly. Not knowing quite what had happened, and perhaps having had a few too many drinks at the Plaza, Daisy drove on without stopping.

I am not going to make excuses for her, but she was young and scared and, like so many rich people, then as now, thought the rules didn't really apply to her, and that somebody would come along to clean up the mess and put things right. That somebody was my father, who came along a few minutes after the accident. He got the whole thing hushed up and kept Daisy out of the headlines. Any thought of Daisy's running off with Gatz was now out of the question. It was never revealed who was driving the 'death car', as the newspapers called it. Apparently Father told the bereaved mechanic that Gatz had been the hit-and-run driver. Perhaps he was covering up for Daisy, or maybe he believed it. To be fair, I don't think my father ever imagined what would come next, but the distraught mechanic found out where Gatz lived and shot him dead in his swimming pool.

Uncle Nick was fond of Gatz, but the unsavory side of his business associations all came out. Wolfsheim was never convicted of anything, but I do clearly remember reading about his sensational murder while I was at boarding school. Wolfsheim was being shaved in a Bronx barbershop when he was shot dead in his chair. Europeans were fascinated with American gangsters in those days, and Wolfsheim's—may I say barbarous demise? —even made the Swiss papers.

Many years later, too many as it turned out, I tried to find the house in which Gatz had lived in that long-ago summer of 1922. But it had long been torn down, replaced with smaller houses. The house that Uncle Nick had rented was gone as well. But our old place across the bay now belongs to a hedge fund manager with whom I used to do business. He was kind enough to invite me to see the old place, but I was too young when we left it to have any memories. It is a marvelous setting, right on the sound with a brand-new dock running out into the sea. Curiously, the hedge fund manager has installed a large green light at the end of the dock, of a type he said was popular in the 1920s. He said the original dock that was there in my parents' day was too small to take his mega yacht, and had to be replaced. But the house, he said, had been restored to its original splendor.

With the Gatz affairs causing so much publicity, my parents decided to pick up and move to France, along with me and Miss MacDonald, my nanny. When things weren't going well, my parents' way of handling it was to move to another city or another country. My earliest memories of life are of our departure from Manhattan on the old French Line steamship *France*. Aunt Jordan came to see us off, but not Uncle Nick, who was angry at my parents, fed up with New York, and moving back to Minnesota. I remember being startled by the powerful blast of the ship's horn as we inched away from the pier. I remember, too the Moorish-style pantaloons of the waiters in the Salle Mauresque.

We had two of the Cabines de Grand Luxe, which my mother seldom left because the crossing was very rough and the *France* was known as a 'bon rouleur'. Even in the calmest seas her swaying passage would sweep crockery from the tables and send all but the most seasoned sailors to the lee rail. While Daisy was seasick, my father spent his time in the bar, drinking the famed Chambertin Burgundy on which the ship prided itself. On the third day out, Tom got into a bar fight and had to be restrained by junior pursers.

Daisy suspected that Tom was making passes at Miss MacDonald during the crossing, which may explain why Daisy sent her packing back to Fifeshire when we landed, to be replaced by the first of many Mademoiselles of my childhood.

The City of Light was quickening its pace after the war years and was gayer and more energetic than it had been just a couple of years before. My mother noticed that there were very few young Frenchmen of her age, so many having been killed in the trenches. But the town churned with all sorts of interesting foreigners: Americans, British, and Russians fleeing their revolution. In those early postwar years, everything that was new in the arts flourished, and Paris was where it was all happening. There were so many Americans in town, escaping from the bourgeois life at home and prohibition, that one restaurateur was heard to say, "Paris, n'est pas encore une colonie Americaine." Paris is not yet an American colony, but for many Americans it was just that.

It was a time when artists, writers and musicians all wanted to break away from the past and experiment with the new. As Daisy's new friend-to-be, Gertrude Stein said, "Paris was where the twentieth century was." The French were fascinated with everything new and modern that America seemed to represent. Americans were seen as rich and glamorous, and every ocean liner disgorged more and more. Daisy was an instant hit when she danced the latest American crazes, and she threw herself into the new role she wanted to play: the avant garde hostess of the moment, with Tom's money to carry it off. She studied hard to reinvent herself and soon mastered a superficial knowledge of music, painting, and dance. Tom had absolutely no interest in art of any kind, but with their money, her charm, and his rough bonhomie, the Buchanans entertained lavishly. Gertrude Stein, however, warned Daisy that Tom was a brute and 'inaccrochable', unhangable, like a painting that was so bad you couldn't hang it on the wall. There would come a time when Daisy would remember that comment with some bitterness.

Chapter 2

Daisy's diaries make it clear that she meant to put behind her the mindless and frantic pace of Long Island in the twenties. She never had much of an education beyond Miss Longworth's school for young ladies in the rolling countryside outside of Louisville, but she wanted to become 'interesting', to have wild and perfectly brilliant friends, poets and artists, not like Tom and Gatz, who were "so impressed with having things," she wrote. She set forth to immerse herself in the great confectionery store of the arts that Paris had become. Stein, with her bulky body and hair cut short, and a face that journalists described as looking like a Roman emperor's, made a big impression on Daisy. Stein was said to be on the cutting edge of the avant garde, just where Daisy wanted to be. Stein's apartment on the rue de Fleurus was warm and full of modern art, which Stein had been collecting for most of the century. Stein, with her voice as low as a man's, was friendly to Daisy, but her companion, Alice Toklas, was not.

Aside from Toklas, Daisy seemed to charm everybody, and she made it her business to get connected, first with Gerald and Sara Murphy, two Americans who seemed to know everybody, and then with the young songwriter Cole

Porter, with his bulging eyes, and his wife, Linda. Both Gerald Murphy and Porter had been just ahead of my father at Yale, and Murphy had also been a Bones man. Porter had been so impressed with my father's prowess on the football field that he'd actually written a song about Tom Buchanan while at Yale. It seems that my father had a party turn he liked to do, barking and growling like Handsome Dan, Yale's bulldog mascot, thereby earning the nickname 'Bulldog Buchanan', as much for his bulldog imitation as for his athletic ability. Porter's ditty 'Bulldog, bulldog, bow, wow, wow', is still sung by sentimental old graduates at football games in New Haven to this day, I am told.

Murphy had a soft face and was extremely dapper, wearing suede gloves, a felt hat and swinging a Malacca cane. He spoke strangely, in an ornate manner. Instead of saying "let's take a walk in the park," Murphy might say, "Methinks we should stroll in yon sylvan glade." Sara, on the other hand, was much more down-to-earth, but bewitching nonetheless. Gerald always went to elaborate lengths to choreograph his life and the lives of his friends. He made even the smallest events into ceremonial occasions. Daisy recorded that every morning when his guests on the Cote d'Azur decamped to the beach, there would be sherry at the ready, with tiny crystal glasses which he would carry down, carefully wrapped in a towel.

Daisy treasured her invitations to spend summer days with the Murphys in their 'Villa America' on Cap d'Antibes, a magical, art deco Moorish house with a large garden of lemon trees, oranges, and mimosa. And towering over it all were cypress trees like minarets overlooking Golfe Juan with the Esterel rising purple in the distance. It was the Murphys and the Porters who invented the summer Riviera, the fashion being theretofore to spend the winter in the South of France. She and Tom would take the Blue Train down from Paris whenever the Murphys summoned them. But when Tom accidentally broke one of Murphy's sherry glasses, Murphy became visibly, and, Daisy thought, unnaturally upset, as if Tom had awakened Murphy from a dream theater in which all his guests were expected to play their parts.

Some years later, toward the end of her life, Sara showed me a bread-and-butter letter that Daisy had sent them, undated, but perhaps written in 1924. "Darling Sara, you and Gerald always make life seem so pretty." I think that one of the reasons that Daisy and the older Sara, with her slanting blue eyes, got along so well is that they recognized in each other the ability, without making any effort, to have people love them and be drawn to them, as if caught in a magnetic field.

Later on, when life was no longer pretty and the Murphys' two sons had died, Gerald was to say that only the made-up part of life had any meaning. He had fled New York and his responsibilities to his family's haut-bourgeois shop in Manhattan, Mark Cross, to become a painter in Paris. He was a good painter who never got the recognition he deserved. I have one of his best: An enormous eighteen by twelve-foot painting of an ocean liner's funnels, which he entitled Boat Deck. I was able to get it out of France into Switzerland just before the war, but I haven't the wall space in any of my houses to hang it, especially not in my chalet in the Oberengadin, where I never go anymore now that I am so old. I have to think about what to do with it, and my other Gerald Murphy paintings, when I die.

I gather that Gerald and my father never liked each other, despite their fraternal Bones bond. Tom would call Gerald a fag behind his back, but Daisy was so attractive and charming that the Murphys put up with Tom. Sara told me that Gerald loved to listen to Daisy's somewhat Southern voice, and that he would adopt her slight stutter in the unconscious flattery of imitation.

Cole and his wife, Linda, introduced my parents to Serge Diaghilev, and Daisy persuaded Tom to put some money into Diaghilev's dance company, Ballets Russes, which was all the rage in Paris. The Buchanans also invested in a nightclub called Le Boeuf sur le Toit, named after the ballet of the same name. Le Boeuf became a favorite of Americans in Paris, so far away from Prohibition America. Daisy, with a musical ear, began very quickly to pick up the French language which utterly eluded my father. Tom never learned French, and when Daisy would prattle on he would just have more to drink.

It seems that Daisy had a brief fling with the Belgian mystery writer Georges Simenon, a handsome man with a long face and intense eyes whom she met at the Boeuf one evening. Simenon had a flat in the Place des Vosges where the two would meet for the occasional assignation when his wife, Tigy, was away. It wasn't entirely satisfactory. The inventor of the fictional Inspector Maigret asked too many probing questions, Daisy wrote in a letter to Aunt Jordan. He made Daisy feel she was being interrogated by Maigret himself. Simenon told Daisy that he had an insatiable hunger for women that had to be satisfied three or four times a day. Daisy found this fanciful. The fling didn't last long, as Simenon soon took up with another transatlantic transplant, Josephine Baker, the Black American singer who was taking Paris by storm.

All Paris was singing Baker's *La Petite Tonkinoise*, about a Vietnamese girl.

"Je suis vive, je suis charmante

Comme un p'tit z'oiseau qui chante."

(I am lively, I am charming like a little bird that sings.)

Earlier Daisy had seen Baker in her Revue Negre, and watched her dance naked behind a feather fan. Simenon said of Baker's derriere, "It is the only bottom that laughs." Daisy was not upset about Simenon's ditching her for Josephine Baker. She seldom held any resentment in these matters. Daisy was not a jealous person. She always seemed to be seeking affection, and when people were drawn to her, as they so often were, she responded.

I cannot believe that Simenon ever really cared for her, but he fit the bill as a glamorous and popular writer, which was the world that Daisy wanted to enter. She wrote of how witty he was, and, being Simenon, he pressured her to become his mistress with his usual energy. Perhaps if my father had been kinder to her and more faithful, Daisy would not have gone searching for love in the Place des Vosges. But Father was Father, and faithfulness was not in his nature. One has to conclude that the physical side of love was not all that important to Daisy, something to be given as casually as a compliment or a charming smile.

For a while, Ezra Pound, tall and thin and impressive with his red beard, befriended Daisy. She, in turn, was thrilled to have a distinguished poet in her entourage. Daisy was never sure if it was she herself that attracted writers and artists, or the Buchanan fortune, which some hoped to exploit. Gertrude Stein let it be known that Daisy could not be friends with her if she remained friends with Pound. Daisy was never quite sure of the origins of their hostility, but it was profound. Stein couldn't bear James Joyce either, which Daisy could understand. Pound had called Stein a 'tub of guts', which didn't make matters better. Daisy suspected that the real cause of Stein's hostility, however, was Pound's refusal to pay court to Stein as the reigning queen of the expat scene.

Pound did not remain long in Paris. Saying that it was filling up with too many Americans, he decamped for Italy with his wife and mistress, where he promptly fathered a child with the latter. He soon became a strong supporter of Mussolini, even agreeing to broadcast propaganda on the radio, for which he was imprisoned after World War II. The Americans could not bring themselves to execute him for treason, so they put him into an insane asylum instead. I went to see him in his old age after his release. He was in his upper eighties and said he was unable to remember any part of his Paris years. I didn't believe him for a moment, but there was little I could do to persuade him to disgorge memory.

My parents moved to the rue de Vaugirard, on Sara Murphy's recommendation, so that they could be close to all that was going on. And goings on there were. Most memorable in Daisy's Paris diary was the never-to-be-forgotten party that the Murphys and Daisy threw on a barge moored in the Seine in honor of Igor Stravinsky's ballet Les Noces. Instead of flowers, Sara and Daisy bought a little bag of toys that were strewn on the table. Stravinsky was the first to arrive, to make sure that he was seated next to the Princesse de Polignac, one of his most important financial backers. Alas for Tom, he was seated on the other side of the princess. When she discovered that he couldn't speak French, she refused to talk to him and kept on talking to Stravinsky throughout the dinner. Tom never found out that the princess was a fellow American, a sewing machine heiress, and oblivious to Tom's charms. The princess was romantically involved with one of the Ballets Russes' ballerinas at the time, something Tom would have been rude about had he known.

Daisy was seated between Darius Milhaud and Jean Cocteau, who had collaborated on the Boeuf ballet. Cocteau arrived very late because of his fear of seasickness. He wanted to make sure the river traffic had died down on the Seine before he came aboard. Cocteau, with his strange hair sticking-up as if from electric shock, wrote a short poem about a cat with green eyes for Daisy on the back of a theater program that one of his boyfriends saved for her. Alas, the poem has been lost or I would reproduce it for you here.

It was within the Murphys' magic circle that the Buchanans got to know Pablo Picasso, the brooding Spaniard, on the beach below the Villa America. Daisy thought he was obviously infatuated with Sara. He was barely polite to Gerald but followed Sara around with his staring dark eyes. He persuaded Sara to pose for him nude, which made the straitlaced Sara giggle. She, in turn, persuaded Daisy to pose nude, too, and the stylized, but realistic for Picasso, painting of the two of them together, dressed in droopy hats and pearls and nothing else, is entitled Two Ladies of Antibes. I saw it once in a Picasso retrospective in New York years ago. It has the same rosy glow as his Grand nu a la draperie which you can see in l'Orangerie in Paris. I went to great trouble and expense to buy Two Ladies of Antibes from a dodgy art dealer in Geneva in the early fifties. It hangs today in my dining room on Cap Ferrat, having journeyed far and wide in the years in between, including some wartime years with Hermann Goering. The painting caused a dreadful row between Tom and Daisy when my father saw it. Tom was drinking heavily in those days, and rows were frequent.

Jean Cocteau arranged a lunch with Edith Wharton in her Pavillon Combe, her eighteenth-century villa north of Paris. It started well. Daisy was impressed that Wharton had been given the Legion of Honor, and Tom was impressed that she had been given an honorary degree at Yale. But when Wharton began to quiz Tom about his family and background, Tom reacted badly, thinking he was being condescended to. Daisy thought Wharton was merely interested in him as a character in one of her novels. He drank too much of the overly sweet dessert wine that Wharton served with her fraise du bois and started telling unseemly stories of vulgarity sufficient to make sure Wharton got the message. Daisy was mortified. They were never asked back.

Tom was better with the Hemingways, even though Ernest had a giant chip on his shoulder about rich people. Sometimes Daisy and Tom would take Ernest and his wife, Hadley, to dinner at the Closerie des Lilas, one of Hemingway's favorite cafes just up the street from where they lived over a sawmill. The Lilas was famous for the night a customer fired a revolver at the mirror to gain the attention of a young lady. "Now that the ice is broken, we can talk," he said, the word for 'mirror' and 'ice' being the same in French. But taking the Hemingways to dinner only made Ernest uncomfortable. This got better when Hemingway came into a bit of money on his own, but the chip never really left his shoulder. Many years later, shortly before he died, he wrote disparagingly in a memoir, published posthumously, about rich people having tried to ruin his talent. The disparagement was clearly aimed at the Murphys and the Buchanans, although he never mentioned them by name. It horribly hurt Sara and Gerald's feelings. Their biographer Amanda Vaill described it as the 'equivalent of a poison pen letter sealed years ago in a bottle that had only just then washed upon the beach'. But in Paris and Antibes in the twenties that mean streak had not become so apparent as it later did.

It seemed to Daisy that Hemingway, too, had a crush on Sara, although Sara never let that get out of hand. He made a pass at Daisy while they were taking a late twilight dip in that lavender sea off Antibes, but Daisy had too much affection for Hadley to reciprocate at that time. Perhaps inevitably, Hemingway challenged Tom to a boxing match. Hemingway was overly proud of his boxing skills and itching to have a go at a rich Yale athlete whom he despised and perhaps envied. Gerald, delighted at the idea, found some boxing gloves in Nice and produced a Chinese gong for a bell to count the rounds. The fight was scheduled for the following evening before cocktails in the garden of the Villa America. All of the Murphys' guests gathered around a makeshift ring concocted of sailor's ropes that Gerald found in the port. Ernest was the better boxer, but Tom was cat-quick and managed to bloody Hemingway's nose in the first round. Gerald called off the fight and declared it a draw, but neither Hemingway nor my father was gracious about it and both refused to shake hands. Ernest was still talking about that fight decades later, insisting that he would have won had Gerald not called it a draw.

Mornings at the Villa America always started with the aforementioned sherry and perhaps a swim, for those not too hungover, on a little beach called the Garoupe which was so prone to seaweed that Gerald, whom we children called Dow-Dow, raked it every day before his guests awoke. The Murphys' villa and those enchanting summers are among my earliest memories. I got along well with Honoria, the Murphys' daughter, a little older than I, but nice to me. We both thought her brothers brats.

When the Fitzgeralds came south that summer, Daisy thought Scott was a hopeless alcoholic and his wife, Zelda, unhinged. Scott was already a successful writer and much better known than Hemingway. Scott admired Hemingway and treated him as a protege, but Hemingway wasn't nice about Scott. Hemingway told Tom that Scott had the long-lipped mouth of a girl. "The mouth worried you until you knew him and then it worried you even more," he said. But then Ernest also said Scott's talent was as 'natural as the pattern made by the dust on a butterfly's wings'. Their first meeting had not been fortuitous. Ernest met Scott in the Dingo Bar in Paris, where Scott passed out and had to be carried home. But Hemingway and Tom thought Scott insufficiently manly.

Daisy wrote in her diary that Zelda was sullen and remote most of the time, and quite possibly mad. One evening the entire household was roused when Scott, in his pajamas, woke everybody up saying Zelda had swallowed too many sleeping pills and was dying. Sara tried to pour some olive oil down Zelda's throat, but Zelda awoke and told her to stop. "If you drink too much olive oil, you turn into a Jew," Zelda said.

There was an outrageous scene at a seaside restaurant in Juan les Pins toward the end of the summer when Scott, drunk as usual, threw glass ashtrays around the room and Tom, equally drunk, threw a glass of red wine in Scott's face, ruining his white linen suit. Whereupon Zelda took off her dress and jumped into the sea. Tom, making a spectacle of himself playing the gallant, jumped in to save her. Daisy thought Tom might be having an affair with Zelda, but then everybody but Scott knew she was having an affair with a French aviator. "Adorable Edouard," Zelda called him. Daisy thought Edouard a crashing boor, especially when he flew his machine low over the villa at nap time.

Hemingway swallowed his dislike of my father and, being fond of Daisy, invited them to join what he called his 'feria mob' at the festival of San Fermin in the Spanish Basque town of Pamplona. It was to be a week of bullfighting and carousing, so I was left behind in Paris with Mademoiselle. Hemingway took great pleasure in explaining to everybody what bullfighting was all about. He insisted that they all go down to the railway yards in the early morning to see the bulls arrive to be unloaded into cattle cars: snorting, wild-eyed, heavy shouldered animals full of menace before the spectacle of their ritual death.

Hemingway pointed to the spot between the shoulder blades where the matador would have to insert his sword if he was to make a clean kill. Daisy was impressed and surprised at how much she enjoyed the spectacle every afternoon, having never seen a bullfight before. Father would mutter that Hemingway was a blowhard and a big phony. Both were prone to belligerency and always seemed on the verge of another fist fight. It was the custom, then as now, to let the bulls run through the streets of the town on their way to the bullring, with daredevil young men running before them. Of course Hemingway and Father competed to see who could run faster and closer to the horns of the stampeding bulls. Daisy thought it was thrilling. Dressed in white trousers with a red sash around their waists, the men would dance in the streets in rope-soled shoes to the raucous music of the 'riau-riau', drinking raw wine out of swollen goatskins until the dawn.

After a few days in Pamplona, an English woman named Duff Twysden showed up, hard, aristocratic, with a statuesque figure, gray eyes, close-cropped blond hair, and a profoundly serious drinking problem. She was offensively condescending to Daisy, who was a few years younger and a lot prettier. There was a good deal of sexual tension in the air. An American literary publisher named Harold Loeb, a dissolute Scotsman named Pat Guthrie, Hemingway, and Tom all seemed to be vying for Twysden's attention. Loeb and Hemingway almost came to blows over her but sensibly backed down and returned to the bar. Daisy felt humiliated, for there was nothing subtle in Tom's attention to Twysden. He'd never made his quests so public before. And say what you like, Twysden was a cut above my father's usual chambermaid conquests. Tom and Daisy had a bitter row in their hotel room that night, screaming at each other so loudly that Cayetano Ordóñez, the matador they had watched kill bulls that very afternoon, came into the room and intervened, almost getting into a fight with the drunken Tom. I say 'almost', because although Ordóñez was no match for Tom in size and weight, Tom recognized that he was a killer by trade and backed down. That afternoon Daisy had been impressed with Ordóñez's grace and the deadly skill with which he dispatched his animals. She had been enchanted when Ordóñez had thrown his matador's hat in her lap and then given her the bull's ear he had been awarded.

No sooner had Ordóñez left the room than Tom turned on Daisy and hit her hard with the flat of his hand. This had never happened before, although they had had screaming matches in the past. Daisy stormed out of the room, only to be comforted by Ordóñez in the hallway and later in his room. And, as he was not yet twenty, this had never happened to him before.

Early the next morning she slipped away to the train station with a red welt on her cheek that she didn't want anyone to see and returned to Paris. I remember her arrival, and Mademoiselle's gasp when she saw the red welt. But Mummy made up a charming story for me about having met an elephant on the train, and because the compartment was so cramped, the elephant had accidentally knocked off her hat and hit her cheek with his trunk when asked by the conductor to produce his ticket. It turned out that my father and Duff had slipped off to spend a week together in Biarritz before he returned to Paris. Although my parents didn't know it yet, and wouldn't for several more years, their marriage was over.

Daisy confided in her diary that maybe she had made a mistake in that summer of 1922, staying with Tom when Gatz reappeared and asked her to run away with him. Maybe if she had left Tom for Gatz her hit-and-run 'accident' driving home, killing Tom's mistress, might never have happened, and Gatz would still be alive.

Traveling to Madrid to research this book, I took that tattered old bull's ear that Daisy had left pressed in a book when I went to see Ordóñez. Alas, although not yet sixty, he lay dying. He remembered the ear and he remembered my mother, but he was not as forthcoming as I had hoped. He urged me to go and see his son fight, for his son had become a matador too. I never did. Unlike Daisy, I loathe bullfights, but I understand that his great-grandson is carrying on the family tradition. I took the ear back to Cap Ferrat and buried it in the garden.

Coincidentally, soon after my visit to Madrid, I ran into Harold Loeb at a party at Peggy Guggenheim's in Venice. He confirmed to me the details of that time in Pamplona and some of the details of life in Paris in the twenties when he had known Gertrude Stein and published some of her work in his magazine Broom. Loeb had pleasant memories of Daisy and told me that her low, contralto voice 'had the liquid lilt of a mockingbird singing at the moon'. It has always impressed me how many men remember my mother's voice, like an arrangement of notes that will never be played again.

Tom and Daisy tried to patch up their failed marriage, but it was never the same again after Pamplona. There was another terrific row in Stein's apartment when Tom noticed some paintings that Picasso had brought over for her inspection. Among them was Two Ladies of Antibes, and my father had a fit, accusing Daisy of all sorts of infidelities and misdemeanors. Gertrude Stein, having never liked Tom, ordered him out and told him never to come back. And he never did.

Soon afterward, with the decade and their marriage dying, they moved to England and perhaps a fresh start. Tom bought the famous and beautiful estate Chessington Place in Gloucestershire, with its Capability Brown gardens and a ha-ha at the end of the lawn. Tom began playing serious polo again and had a stable full of polo ponies. I got an even smaller pony of my own, on which I rode over the endless Chessington acres with a groom running along beside me to make sure I didn't fall. Tom and Daisy bought a flat in Mayfair for the social season. Tom's athleticism and philistinism made him a better fit with the English upper classes than he had been in avant garde, artistic Paris. He felt right at home, joined White's, and in no time became chummy with the Prince of Wales, a fellow polo player. Those young Englishmen who had survived the war, and their young women of fashion even more so, were determined to cast aside the stuffiness and restrictions of the prewar generation. And who better to cast them aside with than two very rich and attractive Americans?

The old king, George V, disliked all things American, which is one of the reasons the Prince of Wales took up with the Buchanans. Another aristocrat who wanted nothing to do with Americans was the Duke of Buccleuch, supposedly a distant relative of Daisy's, whom the Buchanans met at one of the Duke of Westminster's shooting parties. It was quite an affair, with men loading shotguns while dressed in green velvet jackets and waistcoats with white breeches. Daisy counted eight gamekeepers, also in green livery, along with teams of hired beaters to drive the birds onto the guns. Guests arrived in Daimlers, Bentleys, and Rolls-Royces. The shooting itself was for men only, but the ladies, including Daisy, were brought up at lunchtime in a private narrow-gauge train to inspect the mounds of dead birds in their hundreds. Tom was an excellent shot, and Buccleuch was impressed with the heaps of fallen fowl at Tom's feet. Later in the weekend, Tom, as was his wont, overplayed his hand and claimed kinship to the duke through Daisy. The duke was having none of it and cut Tom dead, later complaining to Westminster that Tom was a bounder.

The Prince of Wales shared with Tom an interest in the writings of J.P. Goddard, whose book The Rise of the Colored Empires, was circulating in England and America at the time. Neither the prince nor Tom could be called a reader, but Tom had read the book in America and presented the Prince with a copy. Goddard's call to action to the Nordic races appealed to both of them. "It is up to us, who are the dominant race, to watch out or these other races will have control of things," an agitated Tom expounded to the prince. The future king agreed and said that when he was king he would be in a position to keep the colored in their place for the sake of empire. Daisy shared none of Tom's fierce prejudices beyond a certain condescension when she used the word 'darkies'.

Ever the chameleon, Daisy shifted gears. Now living in England she dropped her Paris persona as avant garde patron of the arts to become the rich hostess of country house parties and the London society scene. The Buchanans fell easily into the Prince of Wales's circle, giving expensive parties and dancing at the Kit-Kat, or at the prince's favorite, the Embassy Club. The prince, it seems, had an eye only for married women, to the despair of the king and queen, who wanted the future king to settle down and produce an heir. Daisy learned to her amusement that it was the custom in the prince's circle for any married woman to leave her hearth, home, and husband for an evening any time the prince should summon. As it happened, the call from the palace came at a time when Tom was being particularly boorish and indiscreet with chorus girls. Would Mrs. Buchanan be free to drop by York House in St. James' Palace for an early supper? Daisy couldn't resist getting even with Tom in such a spectacular fashion.

Daisy's diary brings the scene alive. A poker-faced policeman lets her in by a side entrance. He has seen all this before. The prince's apartments are overstuffed and Victorian, which surprised Daisy. A coal fire is burning in the grate even though the rooms are overheated. Champagne and caviar appear with chopped onions and crust-less toast. The supper consists of cold bird and claret, served by equally poker-faced attendants who never look her in the eye. The prince's conversation is banal and stilted. He is not the bon vivant that he appears to be on the dance floor of the Kit-Kat. Daisy notices how lost, even frightened, his face looks in repose. The preliminaries are perfunctory and the prince leaves something to be desired as a lover. Afterward, the curtain comes down and the performance is never repeated. Daisy is relieved to be in the cool air outside of St. James'.

Daisy did ask with her American bluntness why he had never married. He replied that none of the marriageable girls he met had "stirred my blood or been sentimentally drawn to me. This is not to suggest," he said, "that my emotions have escaped being moved. There have been moments of tenderness, even enchantment," including the one just concluded, without which a princely existence would have been almost intolerable. "But as far as marriage is concerned, I am determined not to be hurried," he told Daisy. It would take another American to hurry him. The prince confessed to Daisy that, although he considered himself good at being a prince, he was really not cut out to be a king, a confession that turned out to be all too true.

Happily for Daisy, the prince's primary mistress at this time, Viscountess Thelma Furness, did not mind this droit du seigneur on the part of the prince. Thelma, who pronounced her name 'Telma' in the Spanish fashion, was an American herself and had been married to an American before she met and married Marmaduke, the first Viscount Furness. She and Daisy got on famously. Thelma and the prince had been on an African safari together, and the prince fell for her 'both in and with the bush', as she delicately put it. Thelma wanted to know all the details of Daisy's nuit d'amour at York House.

Of course, I knew nothing of this. I learned it only from Daisy's diary, which I inherited along with her money. I do remember the Prince's coming to Chessington Place for a shooting weekend. He brought me a doll, but I remember thinking he was too short to be a king, especially when compared to my father, who was my idea of how a king should look. In due course, I inherited Chessington Place, but having no intention of living in England, I sold it. I believe it is owned by an Arab today, or then it might be a Russian.

In 1930, the prince persuaded the king to give him Fort Belvedere, on the grounds of Windsor Great Park. "What could you possibly want with that queer old place?" the king asked his son. "Those damn weekends I suppose." The king did not approve of the growing custom of going away for weekends, which of course made the prince love weekends all the more. Tom and Daisy were invited often, and after dinner the prince would put some American records on the Victrola for dancing. Aunt Jordan sent Daisy all the latest recordings from America, which were a big hit at Fort Belvedere.

It was at the fort that Tom and Daisy met another American, named Wallis Simpson, a friend of Thelma's whom she had introduced to the prince. Before sailing for America for a brief visit, Thelma instructed her friend to 'look after the little man' while she was away—a fatal mistake as the world would soon learn. But never mind; Thelma would console herself in the arms of Prince Ali Khan.

The early thirties saw the effects of the Great Crash on Wall Street creep into the daily lives of working men and women in Britain as well as the United States. Factories closed and lines of hungry, out-of-work men lining up for food handouts grew. The prince, to his credit, showed sympathy for the poor, which increased his popularity. The Buchanan fortune was hit hard but was so vast that Tom and

Daisy were shielded from the onrushing Depression. Tom had to let a couple of footmen and the odd gamekeeper go, but aside from that their lifestyle did not noticeably change. My pony departed, along with my groom, but by then I had outgrown my interest in horses.

For Daisy, the chameleon, another great change of roles was about to take place. Left wing ideas were growing fashionable among intellectuals in London, and much as she had reinvented herself in Paris, and then again in England, now, as the world crisis deepened, Daisy began to immerse herself in socialist and Marxist ideas. I won't pretend it began with an interest in the poor. Daisy, at least at first, showed no interest in the poor as individuals. But when defending the poor in the abstract became chic, at least in some circles, Daisy climbed aboard. It may have helped that Tom was so vocally unsympathetic toward the working classes. Empathy was not one of my father's traits, and the estrangement between him and my mother deepened with the economic crisis.

Daisy began spending less and less time in the country, and more and more time in their London flat. Fewer and fewer of the smart set were invited to her small dinner parties, while the guest list of left-wing authors, politicians, and academicians from the London School of Economics grew. She financed more than one author and subsidized several publishing houses. Tom, on the other hand, remained in Gloucestershire playing polo with weekends at Fort Belvedere.

Tom and Wallis got along famously, and she saw in Tom an ally and steady oak to lean on in the forest of disapproving Englishmen who frowned on her growing relationship with the prince. Daisy thought that one of the reasons the prince was attracted to Wallis was because she seemed to take a genuine interest in his work, such as it was. At dinner parties, Wallis would quiz him about his visit to workingmen's clubs in Leeds or his social schemes for the unemployed. Most of the women in the Belvedere set had little interest in workingmen's clubs, or, for that matter, Leeds, and the prince seemed genuinely grateful.

There were skiing parties in Kitzbuhel and cruises in the Mediterranean to which the Buchanans were invited but only Tom would go, leaving Daisy behind in London with those people of whom he so disapproved. The prince confessed to Tom his love for Wallis, saying, "The hope is forming that I might be able to share my life with her, but just how I do not know." For under the terms of the Royal Marriages Act of 1772, the king and Parliament had veto power over whom the prince might marry. And since Wallis had already been divorced once, and would need a divorce again to marry the prince, there was little chance that the Archbishop of Canterbury would countenance the prince's marrying her. Indeed, when his father died and he became King Edward VIII, he said, in effect, to hell with Parliament and the archbishop and promptly abdicated, creating a royal scandal and a constitutional crisis. But as fate would have it, Daisy was, far away in a country at war. As for my father, his friendship with the Prince of Wales grew with the coming to power of Adolf Hitler in Germany, a man much admired by both. The new German chancellor seemed to embody everything J. P. Goddard was promoting. Thelma told Daisy that Wallis had had a brief affair with Joachim von Ribbentrop, the smarmy champagne salesman who had become Germany's ambassador to the Court of St. James. But given the jealous source, whom Wallis had replaced in the prince's affections, Daisy tended not to believe it. Daisy, at the time, was taking to Marxism with the same enthusiasm with which she had taken to Dada during her Paris days.

As I grew older I came to realize how dazzling my mother was. "There was an excitement in her voice that men who cared for her found difficult to forget," Uncle Nick wrote to me. I felt very much in her shadow on my rare visits home from school. I am reminded of a little poem that Mary Parkman of the Boston Parkmans wrote about her own mother.

When you are seated here,
And beaux on me come calling,
They much prefer to talk to you,
All interest in me falling.

I may not have been pretty, but in due course I was very rich. In 1933, when I was thirteen, I came into an unexpected inheritance. It seems that James Gatz, who had been murdered eleven years before, had left all his money to me. I have no memory of him, but Uncle Nick said that I was brought downstairs to be shown to guests in that summer of 1922. Very odd, I know, but Uncle Nick said that Mr. Gatz was prone to dramatic gestures. His will had been tied up in courts for many years by claims and counterclaims filed by Mr. Wolfsheim and other Gatz associates, each one dodgier than the last. But with the death of Mr. Wolfsheim, the will was settled in my favor. No doubt my new fortune came from criminal wrongdoing, but don't they say that behind every great fortune there is at least one great crime?

My mother decided to make a quick trip to America to visit her aging parents in Louisville that year. Uncle Nick still did not approve of Daisy, but family was family, and having been in the bond business, he was in a position to help her with financial advice. I still have the postcard that she sent me from aboard the Berengaria en route to New York. I felt very smug knowing that Berengaria was Richard the Lionheart's queen, which I was sure my mother did not know. Daisy was thrilled at the election of Franklin Roosevelt, whom Father instinctively hated. I can remember his nasal tenor voice singing, 'Who, who, who, but Herbert Hoover, to see us through in nineteen thirty-two'.

In America, Daisy connected with Hemingway again and was invited to visit him and his new wife, Pauline, in their house full of cats in the Florida Keys. It seems that Hadley had been unceremoniously dumped, which saddened Daisy, but not enough to keep her out of Hemingway's bed. The flirtation that had begun in Antibes grew to fruition in Key West. Hemingway had begun to tire of Pauline and seemed to enjoy the attention of two women in his life. Daisy and Ernest would drink at Sloppy Joe's bar and would get together without Pauline in Havana at the Ambos Mundos Hotel or in Bimini on his fishing boat. Hemingway tried to interest her in his passion at the time, big-game fishing, as he had in the technicalities of bullfighting. But Daisy didn't take to it.

Hemingway confided all this to me in a rather shy way when I went to visit him in his house, the Finca Vigia outside Havana in the fifties. He was then living with his fourth wife, Mary. It was a lovely setting "of muted tranquility," Mary said, that often caught the breeze. Doves gurgled in the giant ceiba tree outside the front door, so big that it seemed ready to overwhelm the house as if it were the ruins of Angkor Wat. Inside animal heads stared mournfully from the walls. Mary had had a glimpse at the new novel he was writing, set in Venice, which she said was 'banal beyond description'. I was surprised, although Hemingway was never my favorite author. Understandably, I think, I always preferred Fitzgerald's writing.

One day when we were out on his boat, Hemingway gave me a bit of information that is mentioned nowhere in Daisy's letters or diaries. It seems that Hemingway was dying to own a fishing boat when he lived in Key West but was strapped for cash. Daisy promptly wrote out a check, swearing Hemingway to secrecy. Hemingway bought a boat and named it Pilar, a pet name for Pauline, who never knew that Daisy had paid for it. He said he returned the money when he was able but was forever grateful to my mother. I am told that today the Pilar is up high and dry on the Finca Vigia tennis court. A sad end to a lovely boat.

Chapter 3

I will interrupt this narrative for a moment to bring you up to date on Nick Carraway, my beloved uncle, Nick, who wrote to me so often when I was a young schoolgirl far away from home. He moved back to St. Paul, Minnesota, after that ruinous summer of 1922, turning his back on New York, Long Island, and the East Coast in general. He felt at the time that he, and others from west of the Ohio, were 'perhaps possessed with some deficiency in common' which made them subtly unadaptable to life on the East Coast. But in 1926, he got restless and decided to give Wall Street another go. He made a lot of money in the next three years, as everybody was doing, but unlike so many others, he got out just in time before the crash in 1929 with a fortune intact.

Uncle Nick met the Berengaria on the Cunard pier when Daisy arrived in New York. If he had not forgiven her for her role in the Gatz murder, which infuriated him at the time, he was willing to put it aside. He was very much amused when Daisy told him of Tom's bumbling attempt to claim kinship to the Duke of Buccleuch. He wasn't at all surprised to hear of Daisy's estrangement from Tom. He had grown to dislike my father, although he never told me that. For Daisy, it was a thrill to be back amongst the tall buildings again, the constant flicker of men and machines in the ever-moving city, used as she had become to the more staid streets of London. She was excited to see through her newly acquired left-wing lenses the slow shuffling of broken men in bread lines or lining up seeking employment that was never going to be tendered. The frostbite of the Depression had wilted the hothouse flower of American optimism that had smelled so sweet in the previous, orgiastic decade of the twenties.

Since they had last seen each other, Nick had married and divorced my godmother, Jordan Baker, who had been my mother's closest friend and confidante. Daisy had said in jest that she would arrange their marriage. "I'll fling you together, lock you accidentally in a linen closet, push you out to sea in a boat." And after an off and on relationship, Nick and Jordan had married as if by Daisy's design. Jordan was one of the best women golfers in the country, but there had been rumors that she had moved her ball from a bad lie in an important tournament. Nothing was proved, but the rumors hung over her as a haze dulling the light of her reputation. The bored and haughty face she presented to the world concealed a deep sea of insecurities. She was incurably dishonest, leaving the tops of borrowed roadsters open to the rain and lying about it, refusing to pay tradesmen when she could get away with it.

Then there was the time when she was accused by her hosts of walking off with a little jade Buddha from a grand house where she was billeted during a tournament in Palm Beach. Nothing could be proved, of course, and Jordan denied it. Aunt Jordan never really got caught out in any of these dishonesties until the one that ended her marriage.

Uncle Nick always said that dishonesty in a woman is never something you blame deeply, and they were married in the summer of 1928, having known each other since they met at Daisy's house six years earlier. It was Aunt Jordan's second marriage, she having become bored with her first husband and ready to catch Nick the second time around. The wedding was covered by the popular press with headlines such as 'Love Birdies on the 18th Green'. Tom and Daisy were invited, but they didn't return from Europe for the ceremonies, sending a magnificent Georgian silver tea set as a wedding present.

Some say women's golf started with Mary Queen of Scots, who became addicted to the game in the 16th century. The word caddie, it is said, comes from the cadets she had carry her clubs. As with other rulers in the centuries since, she was criticized for playing too much golf and neglecting her kingdom. By the late 1920s, women's golf was getting established as a serious sport in America, and Aunt Jordan was at the top of the game. Like Helen Hicks, she began to endorse golf equipment and get paid for it. By the late thirties, she was giving Patty Berg serious competition. But there was never enough time for Nick, and the final bogey in their relationship came when she was caught in what the press called a 'love nest' with one of the lads who carried her golf bags. 'The Caddie Is a Cad' was the headline that most disgusted Nick. She married one more time, and divorced again, before settling down comfortably in her late middle age with another female golf pro. Nick never remarried but lived to great old age, to be celebrated in the

Yale alumni magazine as the second oldest member of his class.

In 1940, Nick worked very hard to elect Wendell Willkie, who was running against Franklin Roosevelt for president. Willkie represented the interventionist wing of the Republican Party, which was the cover Roosevelt needed after Willkie's defeat. Roosevelt co-opted Willkie and sent him as his personal representative to Britain. Willkie asked Nick to come along, and the two were wined and dined by Winston Churchill, who was working hard to bring America into World War II. Upon their return, Nick was introduced to Wild Bill Donovan, so named because of his exploits playing football for Columbia as well as on the battlefields of World War I, where he won the Congressional Medal of Honor. He had been tasked with forming an espionage agency to be called the Office of Strategic Services, or OSS, which earned the sobriquet 'Oh So Social' for the number of Ivy Leaguers it hired. Yale, and being a veteran of World War I, made Nick a perfect fit in Donovan's eyes.

The OSS was supposed to think up schemes that were outside the military's conventional thinking, and some of their ideas were just plain silly, such as lacing Hitler's food with female hormones or releasing incendiary bats over Tokyo. Uncle Nick, however, was credited with thinking up one of the most successful deceptions of the war. It became known in the service as Carraway's Greek Sacrifice, after the chess move in which a major piece is exchanged for strategic advantage on the board. Nick's idea was for Donovan to pretend to be a lapsed Catholic in need of spiritual guidance who wanted to be reunited with the

Church in order to cope with his awesome responsibilities. Nick identified a pro-Fascist priest who had served with Franco's Nationalists in Spain, and who also had important Vatican connections with similar political beliefs. The priest, living in Maryland, was recruited as Donovan's private confessor to ease his alleged spiritual agony over the sacrifices he had to make with agents in the field.

With the hook baited, the recruited priest began hearing Donovan's confessions, and Donovan played his part dutifully. In the sanctity of the confessional booth, the supposedly troubled Donovan began to leak little unimportant secrets to the priest. Some were about real operations, but revealed just late enough to prevent any harm done. 'Operation Chessman', it was called, and in due course it was ascertained that the fake secrets were indeed being passed on to Vatican sources who, in turn, passed them on to the Germans. With this back channel to German intelligence achieved, the OSS was able to discredit known German agents in neutral countries by Donovan's telling his confessor that they were secretly working for OSS and that he agonized about their safety. As far as anyone knew, they were loyal to Hitler, but one by one they started to disappear or to be called back to Germany from neutral capitals such as Lisbon, Madrid, and Stockholm to be tried and executed for treason.

When it was clear that Donovan's gullible priest had a firm grip on Berlin's ear, Donovan made his Greek Sacrifice move. He told the priest that he was in spiritual turmoil about sending his agents behind German lines in the Pas de Calais region of France to help the French resistance when the invasion came. He told the priest that there would be a feint attack in Normandy, but that the real invasion would come in the Pas de Calais a few days later. As hoped, the Germans began rounding up resistance networks, and, sadly, a couple of Americans with them, in the Pas de Calais. But it worked. It was one of several deceptions to deceive the Germans about the Normandy landings, and indeed, Hitler fatally held back his reserves waiting for the real invasion in the Pas de Calais that never was to be. Countless American lives were thus saved.

Nick was highly decorated for this and was asked to stay on when the CIA grew from the ashes of the disbanded OSS. But he refused and went back to Wall Street. Although he deeply admired Roosevelt, he remained a lifelong Republican, donating money to the internationalist wing of the party for the rest of his life. Eisenhower considered him for ambassador to Portugal in gratitude for the considerable donations Uncle Nick made to his campaign, but nothing ever came of it. That nice Bobby Guggenheim got the job instead.

As for the miscreant priest, he was never arrested and never charged with treason. He was thought too valuable a conduit to certain reactionary circles in the Vatican to let go. After the war, he unwittingly proved useful in other ways I am not at liberty to divulge. He has since died and gone to who knows where.

As for Uncle Nick, he died peacefully during lunch at the Yale Club in Manhattan while eating a lamb cutlet. I arranged to have him buried quietly in St. Paul. He came to accept Manhattan, but he would never again set foot on Long Island after that summer of 1922.

Chapter 4

After her sojourn in America, Daisy returned to England where her left-wing companions were very excited about what was happening in Spain. One such friend was a tall, stammering former colonial Burma policeman named Eric Blair. He had just published a book called *Down and Out* in Paris and London, under the nom de plume George Orwell. It was a book that had a profound effect on Daisy, as did its author. They met at some Socialist function or other when Blair was teaching at a provincial school and just up in London for the weekend. Daisy discovered that while she had been gadding about on the French Riviera, he had been working as a 'plongeur', a dishwasher, in a dirty Paris kitchen and living in grim digs on the rue du Pot de Fer. He told Daisy that his street was composed of 'tall, leprous houses, lurching toward one another in queer attitudes as though they had all been frozen in the act of collapse'. Saturday nights consisted of drunken brawls and mysterious Arabs conducting equally mysterious feuds about what no one knew, 'fighting them out with chairs and occasional revolvers'.

Daisy was transfixed by Blair's descriptions of the hard lives of the working poor, whom she had never thought about until her transformation as a woman of the left. 'Slaving, sleeping and drinking', was the way Blair described the life he had led. One time a murder had taken place outside his window and he had hardly noticed, going back to sleep quickly. "We were working people," he said. "No sense in losing sleep over a murder."

In England, Blair had lived the life of the wretched in the poorest parts of London and wandered with tramps in the English countryside. Daisy listened to Blair's adventures while dining in terrible restaurants in Kentish Town that he had chosen, often with his new girlfriend Eileen O'Shaughnessy. Blair opened Daisy's eyes to a stratum of life that she had never before considered.

My mother seems to have had an epiphany during her London days without my father, perhaps not the first spoiled rich girl to question her upbringing and attitudes, especially in the desperate Depression days. But few would take it to extremes as Daisy was about to do. Her diaries reflect a growing social consciousness that had been entirely lacking in the previous decade.

In February of that year, elections in Spain returned the leftist government, and, spurred on by Blair, and excited by the promise of revolution in the Spanish air, Daisy journeyed to Madrid hoping to be present in a new, more radical red dawn. She would miss Eric and Eileen's wedding, but they had promised to follow her to Spain as soon as possible. It was quite a leap for a young woman who had never been anywhere without her father or her husband. Now she was very much on her own.

There have been hundreds of books written about the civil war that followed only months after Daisy's arrival, and some of them even mention Daisy. But suffice it to say that by that summer of 1936, there was no compromising between the left and the right in Spain. Turmoil lay upon the land. Political factions attacked each other in the streets, and the assassin's hand was everywhere. On one side were the leftists, dreaming of a worker's paradise, and on the other the Church, industrialists intent on blocking all reform, and, most important of all, the army. The Spanish pot was on the boil.

Mummy bought an enormous Packard car and hired a driver, Luis, to chauffeur her around Spain. It was a powerful car, dark green and 'gleaming with mirrors and windows reflecting a hundred suns', its extra-loud horn like the melodies of hunting horns sounding out across the Castilian plain. Luis was an ardent Communist, short and excitable with an outsized beret constantly perched on his prematurely balding head. His handlebar mustaches and the bright red scarf around his neck gave him a piratical look and declared his politics. He spoke English with an exaggerated accent, half Brooklyn, half Spanish, acquired while working for the Ringling Bros. circus in America. His resume included the feeding and care of elephants, which enchanted Daisy. He chastised her for buying a Packard instead of a Rolls-Royce. The Packard, he said, was the favorite car of the late Tsar Nicholas II of Russia, while Lenin had always preferred Rolls-Royces. After the election, social revolution was in the air and the Communists were becoming more and more influential. Luis informed Daisy that in revolutionary Spain everybody should use the familiar 'tu' form of address, not the more formal 'usted'. She should say 'Salud' when departing, instead of 'adios' (to God), because God was not somebody revolutionaries should invoke.

Daisy found a Spanish teacher, an older, aristocratic spinster who had fallen on hard times and very much needed the money. Daisy always referred to her as Señora Alvarez, never mentioning her Christian name, if she ever knew it. She was, or so she said, a distant, poor relative of the Duke of Alba, whom Daisy had met in the Embassy Club in London years before. Señora Alvarez was not in favor of the 'tu' form of address. Almost six feet tall and dark of complexion with a slight fuzz upon her upper lip, she was a formidable figure. Her Castilian lisp was more pronounced than most, and she spoke slowly and deliberately, perhaps for the benefit of her students, but giving the impression she thought them dim witted.

Alvarez was as disappointed by the results of the February election as Daisy had been thrilled. She and Daisy talked politics, which improved Daisy's political vocabulary, but neither was able to win over the other. It turned out that Senora Alvarez had translated the works of J.P. Goddard from English to Spanish. J.P. Goddard was much admired by the Spanish right. Daisy learned that Señora Alvarez's husband had been an officer in Spain's African Army and had been killed at the Battle of Annual during the Rif War in Spanish Morocco. His pension was not enough to support her, and her long-dead father had lost all his money when the Americans took Cuba away from Spain.

In July of that year, 1936, Señora Alvarez brought news to Daisy with flashing eyes. A group of Spanish generals had declared that enough was enough. They were taking over the country in the name of God, the army, and the honor of Spain. Whereas Señora Alvarez was delighted, Luis was incensed.

When the coup faltered, the generals brought the colonial army over from Morocco to save Spain from the Reds. Luis hoped that the Reds could save Spain from the army. Supported by Hitler and Mussolini, the so-called Nationalists gained ground against the Republicans, or Loyalists, as the government forces were called. Soon the Nationalists were besieging Madrid.

I have always wondered, Was Daisy's conversion to left-wing politics a reaction to my father's ultraconservative views, perhaps intended to spite my father? There are references here and there in her diaries to how much Tom would have hated this or that in revolutionary Spain. Or was it just her desire to be relevant in a changing world, embracing the latest fad or fashion adopted by people she thought 'wildly interesting?' Whatever her motives, as the Spanish war wore on, her diaries began to reflect a true understanding of the plight of the downtrodden. She wasn't so much pro-Communist as anti-Fascist, and began to develop a hatred that went beyond her desire to be accepted in her current leftist milieu. Was she simply growing up and away from the protective carapace of her wealth and social background?

When the civil war began, law and order broke down across the country. Leftists began burning churches, murdering priests, occupying factories, and appropriating property. In Madrid, the wealthy began to fear for their lives. Señora Alvarez came to Daisy shaking with terror and begging for help. It seems that the señora's husband had been a close companion of Francisco Franco during the Moroccan war, and Franco was emerging as the leader of the Nationalist cause. She would not be safe in 'Red' Madrid. So, although Daisy could not agree with her teacher's politics, she could not see her murdered. And saving her appealed to Daisy's romantic nature. So began the brief episode which Daisy called her 'Scarlet Pimpernel' period, after the 1934 film of the same name, in which Leslie Howard, an English gentleman, pretends to be a useless fop to disguise his role in rescuing French aristocrats from the guillotine during the French Revolution. Leslie Howard had become my mother's favorite actor, perhaps because he seemed the opposite of my father.

Many on the political right in Madrid had been arrested when the Nationalists besieged the city, in fear that they would form a 'fifth column'. The Nationalist General Emilio Mola had said he had four columns marching against the Spanish capital and a fifth inside the city, made up of Fascist sympathizers who were ready to rise and help take the city from within. This caused a frenzy of arrests as the Republican government sought to eliminate the enemy within, real or imagined. There were summary executions and arrests every day. Orders to evacuate prisoners in those desperate days when it looked like the city was going to fall to the Fascists were often disobeyed in favor of firing squads.

Daisy set about saving as many of Señora Alvarez's extended family as she could. There were about a dozen relatives, some of which Luis took to the Portuguese and French frontiers in those days when movement was still possible. Luis was at first incensed, saying they all deserved to be shot. But Daisy persuaded him, after assuring him that the Alvarez family might be class enemies, but they were neither Fascists nor Trotskyites, and that it was better to expel them from the country. After all, there was the hope, then, that the French and the British, and maybe the Americans, might help the Republic in this desperate hour, and it wasn't wise to give the world the impression that the elected officials of Spain were murderers. Luis fell for this argument. However, the only country that was ready to help the Republic was the Soviet Union.

As Daisy learned, the Soviets were dead set on shooting not only Fascists but any followers of Stalin's rival Leon Trotsky who might come their way. She took some Alvarez relatives down to Valencia and Barcelona on the Mediterranean, where she hired agents to get her frightened flock aboard British and French ships. The Blairs had arrived in Barcelona, and Eileen was particularly helpful getting visas.

These trips were not without danger. Her passengers were always terrified when the Packard passed through Red zones. But Daisy, imperiously flashing her American passport and pretending to know more Spanish than she did, prevailed in those early days. Sometimes that was not enough, however, and when necessary Luis would step up and play the role they had rehearsed. She described this in her diary. Should the Reds stop the car at a checkpoint and be desirous of plucking the aristocrats from within, Luis was to step out of the car flashing his mustaches and looking fierce. Standing on the running board to give him extra height, he was to address the bloodthirsty assembly in fiery Marxist language. In the manner of a circus ringmaster whipping growling lions and tigers up on their stools, Luis would denounce these Red militiamen as anti-revolutionary divisionists. He, Luis, was taking these nobles down to the coast, to be either tried and shot or deported from the sacred soil of Spain. "Those among you who would dare to interfere with revolutionary justice decreed from the Republic's lawful authorities in Madrid, step forward and give me your names." None did. The dogs having barked, the caravan would move on.

At other times, taking her cue from the Leslie Howard film, she told the revolutionaries in the towns she passed through that her passengers had smallpox and that she was taking them to Valencia for hospitalization. Señora Alvarez, who had been among the first to be thus rescued, swore eternal gratitude, and Daisy told her she would wire money into a London bank to see that she had enough to live on.

Conditions were beginning to deteriorate that summer, and food shortages were common. Nothing could be sharper than the contrast between my father's and mother's lives in that summer of 1936. Father was dining on fresh seafood and drinking champagne in the Adriatic aboard the Nahlin, the yacht that his friend the Prince of Wales, now King Edward VIII, had chartered for a cruise with his pals, and of course Mrs. Simpson. It is said that the new king, on Father's suggestion, ordered all the books in the yacht's library to be put ashore so that more bottles of alcohol could be installed on the shelves. Mummy, meanwhile, was dining on thin soup and turnips in the claustrophobic and garish cellar of the Gran Via Hotel in Madrid. Her room at the Florida, where she was staying on the Plaza de Callao, had been damaged by shell fire from the Fascist guns on

Garabitas Hill outside the city. Years later I heard many stories of Daisy's spunk under fire, tending to the wounded amid the ruins of the university, making bandages, working in field hospitals in those early days of Madrid's torment. The Ritz itself was turned into a hospital, so at least some of Daisy's humanitarian work took place under the chandeliers of the grand ballroom.

As summer was turning into autumn, the news came to Madrid by telegram that Father, during an international polo match at Hurlingham, had fallen under the hooves of a startled horse. He was carried off the field, which turned out to be a mistake, as his neck had been broken by the fall. Moving him was exactly the wrong thing to do. I found out many years later from the former king, then the Duke of Windsor and living not far from me in the South of France, that my father's last words were four-letter swear words. The duke and Wallis told me how much they had enjoyed my father's company and how they had all agreed that Hitler, at least in the beginning, had been greatly misunderstood.

What Daisy felt upon the death of her estranged husband remains a mystery. Her diary on that day contains only two words: 'Tom killed'. Father had loved Daisy, I think, right up until the end. At least, he never cut off her bank account for what must have seemed to him extravagances in a bad cause. Father's body was shipped back to Lake Forest to be buried in the Buchanan plot, and in due course she inherited his fortune, which she immediately put to work buying ambulances for the Republican cause. Each ambulance had painted on the roof, along with a red cross, the words Una Amiga Americana de la Democracia Espanola. I was informed of my father's death by the headmistress of my school in Lausanne, who summoned me to her office and said I might not attend classes for the remains of the day.

Life in Madrid was getting ever more dangerous and stressful. Air raids by German and Italian planes were becoming more common, and there was no sign that the Western democracies were going to lift a finger to help the Republic. General Mola had said that he would not rest until Marxism in Madrid had been 'wrenched out by its red roots'. Mola's Moroccan conscripts and Army of Africa troops were pushing into the city's outskirts, but the city's citizen-defenders, some of them without any training whatsoever, were rushed to the front, and somehow, they held. These quickly formed citizens' militias wore workingmen's clothes, the blue, overall-like 'monos', and different colored scarves to show their allegiance: red for the Communists, red and black for the anarchists, red and blue for the socialist youth groups.

Before the city settled down to a war-weary fight for survival, the revolution was thrilling. Many women thought that, with the end of the class system, the traditional patriarchy had ended as well, and they felt liberated. Women's militias were sent to fight alongside the men in defense of the city. The idea was enormously appealing to Daisy, although she never picked up a gun. What really caught Daisy's attention was a unit of barbers who called themselves the Battalion de los Figaros, even though most of them had never seen, or would see, Seville.

Daisy saw the first International Brigade soldiers come marching down the Gran Via in less-than-perfect formation.

Many of them had fought against each other in the Great War—Germans, Austrians, Italians, French, British, and Americans, but were on the same side now fighting for the Republic. Enthusiastic Spaniards lined the streets shouting 'Viven los Rosos' in the mistaken belief that the Internationals were Russian.

Daisy, like everyone else in Madrid, lived in fear of what the Moroccan soldiers might do to them should the Fascists break through and take the city. Tales of Moroccan atrocities were spread by the Republican authorities to motivate the citizenry. It was no doubt a racist appeal, but then Spain's national narrative involved expelling the Moors in 1492, and the Republicans wanted to harness that narrative to expel them once again. It was the Fascists who had brought the Moroccans over to fight against the Republic.

The city swelled with refugees pouring in from the countryside, cooking in the Plaza Mayor, sleeping in their makeshift tents, even herding sheep down the Gran Via. Daisy began organizing relief for the refugees, a task at which she became adept even though she had no training.

The battle took on a surrealistic bent among the university buildings, a short walk from Daisy's hotel. The faculty of philosophy and letters building was stoutly defended by men who were hardly able to read or write. In the Clinical Hospital, defenders of the Republic would put bombs in the elevators and send them up to floors held by the Nationalists. The institutes of hygiene and cancer were in the front lines, where hygiene was nonexistent, and the war itself a sort of national cancer. The faculties of philosophy, science and medicine were behind Loyalist lines, while Mola's Moors occupied the faculties of architecture and agriculture. Franco's foreign legionnaires enjoyed a reputation for extreme violence. They brought to the embattled university buildings their slogan: "Down with Intelligence, Long Live Death." Opposing armies, in the street-to-street, building-to-building fighting, would leave insults to each other chalked on classroom blackboards, the insults often misspelled. The university buildings were being reduced to pockmarked ruins. In November, the battle settled into a siege when the Fascists decided that to push further into the city would cost too many lives, and the defenders made the same decision about trying to retake lost ground. But the sniping, the machine guns, and the shelling never ceased.

What Daisy hated and feared more than anything were the bombers of Hitler's Condor Legion, unleashing incendiary bombs over Madrid in order to study their effect on a civilian population. Spain itself was becoming a kind of university of war and weapons laboratory, where Germans and Italians learned lessons that would be helpful in the greater conflict to come. Half the city had its eyes constantly cocked to the sky to look for death's approach.

Daisy recorded that the grounds of the old royal hunting lodge turned public park saw trenches and gun emplacements dug where citizens used to stroll. Sometimes the Republican soldiers would fish in the former royal fishponds. During all of this, the loudspeakers of the Republic blared patriotic speeches and songs over the battle zone, along with the cry: "No pasaran!" They shall not pass. And then the Fascists' loudspeakers would answer back.

The most impassioned voice on the Republican side was that of a middle-aged woman from the Basque country named Dolores Ibarruri, known to all as 'La Pasionaria', the Passionflower. Daisy described her as speaking in rough peasant tones with an earthy laugh and great powers of oratory. She had a lively expression while talking but a look of sadness when in repose. People said that with her dark, oaken face, she couldn't be anything but Spanish. She quickly became a symbol of Republican Spain, just as the mythical Marianne had once represented revolutionary France.

The Communists were always the best organized but by no means the most radical of parties on the Republican side. Nor were they the most numerous. "The red tail on the Socialist kite," Daisy said. Anarchists, who believed in no government at all, were far more revolutionary and held a deep hatred of Spain's Catholic Church—the most repressive in Europe. Daisy never understood anarchist theory. "How can they govern if there is to be no government?" She put anarchism down as something important to the Spanish soul rather than a practical answer to Spain's political problems. Stalin and the Communists were afraid that a real revolution would frighten the democracies, so, ironically, it was the Communists who held the revolution back and began purging the more radical elements on the Spanish left, including the anarchists.

Madrid, in its quieter moments, had become a must stop for left-wing war tourists. Daisy was asked if she would show the famous wit Dorothy Parker the war sites, which usually consisted of a tour of the covered trenches in the university grounds. Parker complained about the rats, which

Daisy didn't notice anymore. "Shouldn't they be leaving the ship about now?" Parker asked.

The winter of 1936-37 was a particularly hard time for the Madrilenos, with heat, food, and ammunition in increasingly short supply. The shell fire and the bombing raids never ceased, and the government made an effort to get people to leave the capital. Posters were put up throughout the city saying: "Evacuate Madrid. The government asks you to leave Madrid to the army." But except for a few who sent their children away for their safety, most people stayed on, including Daisy. Her ambulances began to arrive in Valencia and Barcelona, which were in government hands, and they made their way up to Madrid along the few roads that had not been cut by the Fascist forces. Daisy's Packard became a familiar sight ferrying medical supplies across Madrid with Luis giving the clenched-fist salute of the Communists to gawkers on the sidewalks as the giant car passed by.

Hemingway showed up at the Hotel Florida early in 1937, telling Daisy about a wonderful new girl he had met in the Florida Keys called Marty—Martha Gellhorn—just as pretty as Daisy and a good nine years younger. She was an accomplished writer and a friend of Eleanor Roosevelt's, both of which impressed my mother. Hemingway said, "You'll love her. She's tough, Daughter." Hemingway liked to call women 'daughter'.

Just as he had needed to show off his bullring savvy in Pamplona, Hemingway now began to show off his military knowledge. He began calculating the trigonometry of the incoming shell fire. He claimed to know which rooms at the Florida would likely be hit, and he wasn't all wrong. Daisy complained of the granite, marble, and plaster dust from shell-and-bomb-blasted buildings that seemed to hang in the air of Madrid for days. Her hair was never clean. She wrote that the silver lyddite smoke gave her a perpetual cough. She noticed that when a shell hit the Florida, the rats in the walls would become crazed with fear, and the noise of their scuttling and squeaking would continue long after the shells had stopped. Then there was the broken glass that littered the streets all over town, even though most windows were crisscrossed with tape. The tinkle of broken glass appears often in her notes, as it did in her dreams.

Daisy had her own emotional trigonometry to figure out because Gellhorn was expected soon, and Hemingway's constant slang, which migrated from phony American Indian talk to Brooklyn 'youse guys' tough talk, was becoming tiresome. She didn't remember that being an annoyance in her Key West days. She was also disappointed that Hemingway had not come to Madrid to support La Causa. He had come to get fresh material for his writing. He made fun of her new passion for Marxism, saying: "Water closets of the world, unite! You have nothing to lose but your chains." But Hemingway was to become more and more swept up emotionally with the cause as the war blundered on. She had no regrets about Hemingway's having a new love, and in fact was rather relieved. She and Hemingway were still friends, and she never felt sorry for Pauline as she had for Hadley.

They took a drive out from the city to Guadalajara and Brihuega, where the loyalists had defeated three Italian divisions. Hemingway said it was the worst Italian defeat since the Battle of Caporetto in the Great War, a war in which Hemingway had been wounded on the Italian front. Daisy was annoyed that Hemingway kept bringing up his war experiences. His role in the war seemed to grow with each telling. Still, turning back the Italians was important, because it meant that the Fascists could not completely encircle Madrid.

Hemingway was happy to reach the battlefield before it had been cleared of its dead, and so in rain and intermittent snow flurries they found Italian bodies among the mangle of twisted steel that had once been trucks and tanks. Hemingway pointed out to Daisy where the Italians had been desperately trying to dig holes in the stony earth to seek safety from the Spanish Republican guns. They died with their short entrenching tools still in their hands, waxy faced in the rain. Daisy noted that they had on their summer uniforms despite the cold. Mussolini had not properly equipped them for a Spanish winter. "You did damn well, Daughter. You never flinched at the corpses," Hemingway told her in his condescending manner. I am proud of my mother for refusing to call him 'Papa' as he would have liked.

On their way back to Madrid, the Packard came under attack from a German plane. Luis drove the car into a ditch to make the pilot think he had destroyed his target. Nobody was seriously hurt, but Daisy received a gash on her forehead which exactly matched the scar on Hemingway's forehead. They both laughed and Hemingway pretended it had profound meaning. They both carried those scars to the end of their days. A Republican army truck pulled the car from the ditch, bruised but still functioning, and they resumed their journey back to Madrid. Later in the war the

Packard was destroyed in an artillery attack while parked in the street near the Hotel Florida. That ended Luis' employment in my mother's service. After that he joined the Republican army until the war's end, escaped to France, and ended up in Mexico, then Cuba, along with other refugees from the losing side. For a while, he found employment at the Finca Vigia, driving Hemingway, who remembered him from Spain. Then he joined Castro in the Sierra Maestra and, I presume, was killed. At least, I have never been able to trace his whereabouts after that.

A few days after their trip, Hemingway and my mother were dining together at the Gran Via Hotel, sharing a meal of bacalao, the ubiquitous and foul-tasting fried cod of the siege years, when in the door walked Martha Gellhorn. "I knew you would get here, because I fixed it so you could," Hemingway said without getting up from his chair. Martha took immediate umbrage, saying that she had gotten to Madrid on her own without any help from anybody. Daisy predicted in her diary that night that the romance between Ernest and Martha would not last, because Hemingway was too boastful and bullying, while Martha was too prickly and fiercely independent to fit into Hemingway's idea of an ideal mate. Although they did eventually marry, Daisy turned out to be right in the long run. But in the hot-house, supercharged emotional atmosphere of a city under siege, Ernest and Martha's love affair flourished, and Daisy gracefully stepped aside.

I have always been impressed by the lack of jealousy in any of Daisy's diary jottings. She was never possessive about her lovers. She always maintained a curious detachment that made it easier for her and Gellhorn to become friends. Daisy took Martha under her wing. Many years later, when I went to see Gellhorn in Wales, where she lived, she told me she could never figure my mother out. Daisy had been very nice to her when she arrived in Madrid to claim Ernest, too nice Gellhorn thought at the time. Gellhorn was suspicious of Daisy's southern belle manners and at first thought her stutter affected. But then they became good friends, Gellhorn told me, and since Daisy had withdrawn from competition, they fell into the easy friendship of two good-looking women sharing hardships in a war zone. By the time I met her, Gellhorn held such a bitter resentment of Hemingway, whom she finally divorced, that she refused to speak his name.

By April of 1937, the war was not going well for the Republic, but Madrid still survived, and the warm weather before the heat of summer was gratefully received after that first grim winter of the war. Flowers began to bloom in the parks, and morale improved.

One day not long after Gellhorn's arrival, John Dos Passos arrived in Madrid. The Republic's press office in Valencia had assigned him a Hispano-Suiza, even grander than Daisy's Packard, to take him to Madrid. Dos, as everyone called him, was one of the most successful writers in America and had been on the cover of Time magazine. The press office was attentive. Daisy had always liked Dos, with his shy manner, his mournful brown eyes, whom she had met while staying with the Murphys in Antibes in the twenties. Dos had not really approved of the Buchanans and actively disliked my father. But he had liked my mother even though he didn't take her seriously. Now that Daisy was no longer the frivolous girl she had seemed Dos took another look. One of his reasons for coming to Madrid was to collaborate with Hemingway on a film to be called *The Spanish Earth*. Knowing of Daisy's wealth, Dos asked her if she might help financially. Daisy immediately said she was in and would be glad to contribute in a major way.

Trouble came when Dos and Hemingway disagreed about what the main thrust of the film would be. Dos wanted it to be about the suffering of the Spanish people at war, while Ernest wanted to keep the focus on the military. Daisy agreed with Dos. Since the film was basically a propaganda film, she felt that his approach would move more people. To guide the film through to completion, a corporation of backers was formed, to be called the 'Contemporary Historians'. The group was to include Lillian Hellman, the playwright; the poet Archibald MacLeish; Dos; Ernest; and Daisy. Gerald Murphy, in New York, promised to lend the venture his Spanish music records for the film's soundtrack. Hemingway would do the narration.

But disagreement over the film's focus wasn't the only trouble. Daisy noticed how rude Hemingway could be to Dos on occasion, how dismissive. They had been friends in Paris and on the Riviera. What had gone wrong? Dos was anything but macho, and Hemingway made fun of his lack of military knowledge.

Hemingway would mutter behind Dos's back that he had 'no balls'. Could Hemingway have been jealous that another famous American writer was there on Ernest's turf? But there was another undercurrent at play. Dos was a friend of Ernest's wife, Pauline, and disapproved of Ernest's open affair with Gellhorn. Hemingway sensed this, which made him all the more unpleasant to Dos.

One could always tell who was sleeping with whom in the Florida, because when the war intruded and shells hit the hotel in the night, customers came out of their rooms in various stages of undress to find shelter in the cellar. Among them, Daisy reported, were the lively ladies whom Hemingway called 'whores de combat'. One memorable time, the gallant French aviator and writer Antoine de Saint-Exupery stood in the dust and smoke during a bombardment, offering each woman headed for the cellar a grapefruit saying, "Voulezvous une pamplemousse, madame?" Grapefruit was in very short supply in Madrid, and Saint-Exupery didn't think he was going to survive long enough to eat his supply all by himself. Indeed, Daisy wrote that she was hungry most of the time and cold that winter. She was glad for a grapefruit.

She was generous with the few luxuries and difficult-to-get delicacies brought up from Valencia with her ambulances. And, of course, liquor.

There were always raucous parties at the Florida. Reading her notes, I have to conclude that the war was a terrific adrenaline high for Daisy and the other foreigners thrown together in a dying city with an implacable enemy at the gates. Hemingway, in particular, seemed in a state of euphoria, and his room became a sort of fraternity house for the International Brigades on leave from the front. Hemingway kept an armoire full of food and a Victrola with dozens of records. When his beloved Chopin records were broken by a drunken member of the Abraham Lincoln Battalion, Hemingway philosophically called it 'desastres de la guerra', after the famous Goya portrayals of Napoleon's war in Spain.

There was little heat, but at least the Florida had hot water some of the time. Gellhorn told me it was so cold that her fingers would freeze at the typewriter keys. Daisy slept in her fur coat, and when the cold seeped in under and around the decrepit frames of the battered windows, she could believe in the old saying that the air of Madrid could kill you without blowing out the candle. Fleas and lice were another torment of life in Madrid, and there was never enough soap. In the hot season, the heat was unbearable, and with the shelling and the air raids the smell of unburied corpses was never far away.

Chicote's bar on the Gran Via was everybody's hangout, packed with journalists, soldiers of the International Brigades on leave, as well as ordinary civilians looking for a little cheer. The place, Gellhorn told me, "reeked in the winter with the smell of wet wool overcoats, black tobacco, and unwashed bodies, and the rain, rain, rain outside." Some nights the crush of bodies was like that of a subway car, mostly men, but Spanish girls, too, in their dyed blond hair and high heels.

A favorite of Daisy's was a young Harvard graduate whom she had met on Long Island fifteen years before. Like Daisy, he, too, had fallen in love with 'la causa', and was on medical leave from the Abraham Lincoln Battalion. He came in on crutches every night and blushed when Daisy asked him how he had been wounded. "It's not even a wound of honor," he mournfully confessed. He had wandered off at night to relieve himself and broken his leg falling into a trench. He appears often in Daisy's diary. She must have been glad to see a friend from the past who, like her, had taken an unanticipated fork in the road. Daisy reported that when his leg healed it was shorter than the other, and that he would have a limp to remind him of Spain for the rest of his life. As it was, that wasn't to be very long. Daisy's diary records that he was killed on the Ebro River front late in '38 just before the Internationals were recalled and sent home.

Another denizen of Chicote's was the French writer Andre Malraux, with his volunteer pilots of the Escuadrilla Espana. Daisy was impressed with these flying Frenchmen who seemed to her like a throwback to the mounted Crusader Knights who stormed off to Jerusalem almost a thousand years before. But then Daisy was a hopeless romantic. She begged Malraux to take her up on a flight, but Malraux just laughed at her.

Despite the bombs and shells, streetcars still ran when the streets weren't too torn up, and people tried to go about their business as normally as possible, even though there was no normality. Nonetheless, cinemas were open, and Daisy wrote of seeing Lionel Barrymore in David Copperfield. She noted the irony of the shell-damaged Paramount theater's playing Charlie Chaplin's film Modern Times as the bombs rained down.

Daisy wrote that people huddling in doorways during an artillery barrage counted the shell bursts, trying to figure out how much time they had before the next high-explosive projectile arrived. She observed one man study his watch and then move quickly down the street, putting up his umbrella even though there was no rain as if it could somehow protect him from the shells, or the bombs that fell when the German Junkers or Italian Caproni bombers would appear in the sky to the despondent wail of air raid sirens and the sound of the pathetically inaccurate antiaircraft fire. There was one of these guns in the plaza near the Florida, and its bangings would be as unnerving as the red dots of tracer bullets in the night were translucently beautiful.

There were always long lines outside shops, which seemed to have less and less food with every visit. People who had been waiting for hours were reluctant to give up their place in line even when the bombers came. To be in Madrid was to always have the rubble from bombed buildings in the streets blocking your way, plazas pocked with new shell holes, and the mangled dead for whom the ambulances came with fresh coffins. Some of the apartment buildings after an intense shelling looked like open drawers spilling out their contents into the street, with bathtubs held only by their pipes on each floor—so many private lives ripped open for all to see. The shells came into Madrid with what many described as a sound similar to the tearing of cloth, only louder. Daisy recorded that the Herald Tribune man Vincent Sheean called the sound 'the swift, beating wings of death'. Jimmy, as Daisy called him, was 'nothing if not theatrical', she wrote. With the front line only a few blocks away, Daisy would walk to the war to help the medics after breakfast. The sound of rifles and machine guns came through the walls and windows of the Florida even with a pillow over your head.

Once an elegant art nouveau structure, the Florida had become a rather beat up and shabby press club. The correspondents living there had a competition for who could come up with the best way to describe the sound of rifles, grenades, and bombs on the printed page. Daisy got a laugh with her pathetic suggestion: "B-b-b-bang." Hemingway called her slight stutter 'the Louisville light machine gun'. The Florida has been replaced now on the Gran Via with a department store. I was lucky enough to visit it before it was torn down in the mid-sixties; the hotel storage room held a trunk full of my mother's belongings, including her diaries, from which I have been able to extract this narrative.

Chapter 5

As Daisy and the war wearied, she found herself spending more and more time at the Gaylord Hotel, where the Russian advisors to the Loyalist side lived. The Russians were becoming more and more important to the Republic as the only international source of arms and ammunition. The Gaylord's food supply was correspondingly superior to almost any other place in town. The hotel's marble lobby and porte cochere were guarded by Spanish soldiers with fixed bayonets. Her particular friend in those days was an unimposing looking man, a Russian, short of height, in wire-rimmed glasses, with crinkly hair and bad teeth, yet for all of that, a man possessed of beguiling charm: Mikhail Koltsov. Officially he was the Pravda correspondent covering the war, but everybody, including Daisy, believed he had a back channel to Stalin. Daisy cared nothing for that but found him charismatic, witty, insightful, and cynical, all of which appealed to her. She called him Mickey. Koltsov also knew a great deal about military matters and was generous with his opinion. It was said of Koltsov that his friendly face and huge head balanced on a small body expressed a kind of enthusiastically gleeful amusement that cheered everyone up no matter how depressing the circumstances. This relentless cheerfulness made him popular with one and all.

Daisy's diaries do not reveal exactly when they became lovers. Known for his indiscreet affairs, Koltsov had a Russian wife and a German mistress with green almond-shaped eyes who took the name Maria Osten, osten meaning 'east' in German, to demonstrate her faith in the Soviet Union. Koltsov could be indiscreet in his political opinions, too, and wasn't above mocking the Communist Party and his fellow Russians who were taking over the leadership of the war and the secret police. His humor, his irreverence, and his gaiety made him irresistible to Daisy. They say opposites attract, but Daisy, the heiress and former debutante who had known the king of England, and Koltsov, the Jewish sophisticate and dedicated Communist from Kiev who was pals with Stalin? War seemed to be the great equalizer, and Koltsov had an undeniable dash about him. Besides journalism, he was expert in flying, too, and had pioneered an air route from Moscow to Ankara, to Tehran, to Kabul in the foothills of the Hindu Kush when aviation was new and Afghanistan the ultimate in remoteness. Like so many Russians, he loved poetry and would recite Russian verses to her from memory, although she could not understand a word. Koltsov was fluent in English but maintained that poetry could only be recited in Russian. According to Daisy, he carried a volume of Pushkin around with him everywhere he went.

Koltsov was an insistent lover, far more so than Daisy. But what really appealed to her was his sense of fun. She reflected that there had not been much laughter in her life with my father. With Mickey, she could relax and be herself. There was no need to appear knowledgeable about Marxist theory. Koltsov didn't give a hoot about Marxist theory. She could ease off from being relevant. The hours together with him were an escape to a world she thought she had lost. A world away from the war, away from responsibility. Above all, he made her laugh. They loved to plan a life together. They would move to Málaga after the war. She would buy a newspaper for him. There would be several for sale after the Fascists had been defeated, and he would document the dawn of a new Spanish society. He, on the other hand, fantasized about living in Paris, of going for coffee at the Select in the mornings. Oddly they never fantasized about living in Russia. Of course, they both knew none of that would ever happen, but it was so much fun to think about it.

Koltsov was very tight with the Republican military and its Russian advisors, and more than once he would leak information to Daisy, instructing her to pass the information on to Herbert Matthews of the New York Times. Thus could Koltsov keep his fingerprints off the sensitive information that he, and presumably Moscow, wanted the American public to know. Too often Matthews' stories would be cut or altered, which he blamed on zealous Catholics on the copy desk who hated the Republic. Koltsov believed that one day America and Russia would be allies against Fascism, and that they would be the last two countries left powerful when the war was over. Most correspondents sensed that Spain was only the curtain raiser to a greater, worldwide war.

Daisy introduced Koltsov to Hemingway, feeling that the two military buffs could be of mutual benefit to each other. Hemingway thrived on inside information, and Koltsov had plenty of that. Instead, the meeting produced one of the weirdest incidents of the entire war, according to Daisy. The occasion was a cocktail party in Koltsov's rooms at the Gaylord, flowing with vodka.

Hemingway brought Martha with him, and before long a Spanish officer was at her side offering her a dish of caviar, of which the Russians seemed to have an endless supply. He was Lieutenant Colonel Juan Guilloto Leon, later general, one of the most talented officers serving the Republic. Very good-looking and trim, he went by the nom de guerre 'Modesto'. He was one of those Spaniards for whom flirting with pretty girls was a duty and a matter of national honor, and here he was with two of the prettiest girls in Madrid.

Years later, Gellhorn told me that Modesto was 'an intensely attractive man' and that she was pleased that he had come to talk to her, one of the few blondes in the room. "Seeing me wolf the caviar, he asked if Daisy and I were hungry. We said we were, like everybody else in Madrid. We were getting on happily with no personal overtones when someone appeared wearing an ugly shark's smile, the first time I had seen it." The shark's smile belonged to Hemingway.

Annoyed at the attention Modesto was paying Martha and my mother, Hemingway began berating him and suggested that they have it out then and there. Whereupon Hemingway produced a handkerchief from his pocket and demanded that, since they were among Russians, he and Modesto put the two ends of the handkerchief in their teeth and play Russian roulette with revolvers at close range—

one bullet for each chamber. The chances were one in six that one would be killed, one in twelve that both would die. As Martha recalled it to me, "He managed a double insult: to me as a piece of female property, and to Modesto as a thief on the prowl." Daisy, however, considered the incident typical Hemingway belligerence that had ruined a good party. For Daisy, it was the first time she had tasted caviar since that long-ago evening with the Prince of Wales.

Modesto rose to the bait, saying, "Vamos," and they headed for the door on the assumption that Russian roulette was better played in the corridor. Koltsov quickly came over and, taking Modesto by the arm, led him away to calm him. Hemingway just smiled and treated the whole thing as a joke, perhaps relieved to find a way out. Hemingway's traits reminded Daisy of my father, traits that she found attractive at first but which later repelled her.

The next day, when Martha and Hemingway were visiting the Casa de Campo front, they ran across Modesto behind a stone wall. Hemingway started asking Modesto military questions as if nothing had happened the night before. Modesto was answering when all of a sudden mortar shells began dropping just beyond the wall. Everyone save Modesto and Hemingway dove for cover. But in an obvious test of machismo, neither Hemingway nor Modesto would be the first to duck. "It was sheer luck that neither was killed or wounded," Gellhorn told me many years later.

She was sure that Hemingway was jealous of Modesto's reputation for bravery and his command of an army. "The boys had to attend to their vanity," she said, "and for Modesto, I suppose, it was a question of Spanish honor." I knew all about that Latin sense of honor, and I paid dearly for it when I divorced my second husband.

As for Koltsov, Daisy was impressed with the efforts he made to save Arthur Koestler, the then-Communist sympathizer who later turned against them, writing his famous novel *Darkness at Noon*. But in 1937, he was all in for a Red revolution. He had rather foolishly, in Koltsov's view, gone to Málaga to witness the Fascist takeover of that city. He had already been expelled once from the Nationalist zone and was therefore known to their authorities. He was immediately arrested and put in solitary confinement in Seville, awaiting a possible death sentence. He could hear the iron doors banging as other prisoners were led out to face the firing squad. He never knew when he would be next.

It was then that Koltsov had his brilliant idea. The wife of an ace fighter pilot, a war hero to the Nationalists, was at that time living quietly in Valencia in the Republican-held zone. Why she was in the so-called Red Zone no one knew. Perhaps it was to visit relatives. Koltsov's idea was to have her arrested with as much publicity as possible, revealing that she was the wife of an enemy ace. The news was bound to get back to the Nationalist side, and it did. This allowed Koltsov to arrange a prisoner exchange, the pilot's wife for Koestler's life. Daisy thought it typical of Koltsov to come up with something inventive to save a friend.

Koltsov knew of a secret plot to assassinate General Francisco Franco, who was now leading the Nationalist fight. It seems that the Communists had an agent on the Fascist side, a foreigner, who could gain access to the general. Koltsov didn't tell Daisy who it was, but many years later it was revealed that the potential assassin was none other than an Englishman, Kim Philby, the Times of London correspondent covering the Fascist side. In the end, the Russians decided that Philby was not cut out for 'wet work', i.e., killing people. Philby went on to become a famous spy for the Russians.

Daisy noticed how Republican government officials seemed to defer to Koltsov, even though he was technically only a reporter. These were the days of vicious purges in Russia, and Stalin was arresting many of his old Bolshevik comrades on trumped-up charges and having them shot. Koltsov, with his usual sense of irony, asked Daisy to tell him all about the seventeenth century witch trials in Massachusetts. When the Soviet ambassador was recalled to Moscow and executed, Koltsov fell into a depression. But his faith in Stalin and the Communist Party never wavered, or if it did he never told Daisy. He said that the purges in Moscow were necessary because "beyond our borders, in the general staffs of the mighty, foreign owners in the palaces of the industrial bosses, in the glittering cabarets and restaurants, strong and subtle plots were being fabricated…to destroy Soviet rule." Stalin himself could not have made the case better. He thought that with Western help, disloyal Russian generals could step in and take over Russia, the way the disloyal Spanish generals were taking over Spain.

When the second International Congress of Writers for the Defense of Culture, organized by the Communists, decided to meet in Spain in the summer of 1937, Koltsov was asked to journey down to Valencia on the coast and give the keynote address to two hundred writers from twenty-six countries in the elegant town hall. It was Koltsov's task to explain to this international gathering what was going on vis-á-vis Stalin's purges, not an easy task. Many intellectuals were having second thoughts about the Soviet Union. What had seemed like the hope of the world to some writers was now looking more like a dank cellar of terror, similar to the days of Robespierre. After denouncing André Gide for a book expressing doubts about the new Russia, Koltsov went on to say that, although it was difficult for foreigners to understand how Soviet writers could support the purges, in fact it was a matter of honor. "The honor of the Soviet writer consists precisely in the forefront of the battle against treachery... we support the government because its hand does not shake when punishing the enemy."

Brave words, Daisy thought, but she knew that Koltsov was deeply troubled by what was going on in his homeland. When the entire congress moved en masse up to Madrid for a few days, Daisy thought it absurd. To risk lives in Madrid, which was under Fascist guns, was foolish, and to find scarce food and drink for so many 'tourist' struck Daisy as slightly obscene.

While anti-Fascism undoubtedly burned bright in Koltsov, he was too clever, too cynical, not to see through much of the humbug surrounding Communist doctrines and myth. In September of the following year, Koltsov left Spain, temporarily he thought, to report on the dangerous situation in Czechoslovakia, which Hitler threatened, and which the Western powers were about to abandon in an orgy of appeasement. Martha Gellhorn, too, made a quick reporting trip to Prague, and found Koltsov sunken and dejected, not the always upbeat and ever-joking comrade he had been. It turned out he had returned to Russia to brief Stalin personally on the events in Spain. Disconcertingly, Stalin started joking with Koltsov, calling him 'Don Miguel', asking him if he had a pistol, and if he was contemplating suicide. Koltsov said, "Of course not, Comrade Stalin," but Koltsov was too intelligent not to see the menace in Stalin's jokes.

And sure enough, Koltsov disappeared toward the end of 1938, never to be seen again. Daisy remembered his offhand remark made in happier days, that everything looked desperate when he wasn't wearing his glasses, and that he must ask the firing squad not to remove them before they shot him. It was a typical Koltsov wisecrack, but what stayed with Daisy was this hint that he knew that eventually he, too, would be swept up and mowed down by Stalin's paranoid purges. She contemplated going to Russia to try to find him, but in the end she saw that that would be a hopeless mission. Maria Osten, on the other hand, did go to Moscow and paid the price for it. For it was revealed many years later that Koltsov had been tortured and then shot in 1940 at Stalin's bidding. One of the charges against him was that he had been too friendly with an American spy in Madrid named Buchanan. The back channel from Koltsov to the New York Times via Daisy somehow became known to Moscow and the ever-suspicious Russians. Maria Osten was charged with being a Nazi spy, and she, too, was tortured and executed.

Daisy thought there might be another reason why Koltsov and other loyal Communists in Spain came under Stalin's disapproval. The German writer and International

Brigadier Gustav Regler held that among the Russians in Spain, "There was none of the slavish terror of the Moscow intellectual. Under the hail of Fascist bullets, they forgot the bullet in the back of the neck, the secret executions…" With service in Spain, Regler wrote, these Russians, "were made whole again. They became new men. The stink of Moscow was blown away by the winds of the Sierra in this heroic Spain." No wonder Stalin hated them. Of course, it didn't help that among Koltsov's lovers had been the wife of Stalin's secret police chief.

At the time, although few knew it yet, Stalin was losing hope that the Western powers would ever stand up to Nazi Germany. So, it made sense to Stalin to sell out Spain and make a pact with Hitler, which he set about doing. Passionate anti-Fascists like Koltsov were becoming an embarrassment.

Meanwhile the situation in Madrid continued to deteriorate. Food was getting ever more scarce, even on the black market. Daisy began making trips down the dangerous road to Valencia to ensure that her ambulances got through. And the cost in bribes kept rising as the Republic's position deteriorated.

Unlike her friends Hemingway, Gellhorn, Dos Passos and Koltsov, Daisy was not filing stories for newspapers and magazines. She would often make herself useful, however, by taking their stories down to the Telefonica building to be passed by the censors before being telegraphed abroad. Since my mother never described what this was like, I rely on a letter that Gellhorn sent me years later:

Filing in Madrid had a certain dash to it. The censor, Ilsa, a stern, dumpy German woman, had her office in the Telefonica Building on the Gran Via. Telefonica was the tallest building in Madrid and was used by Franco's German gunners on Garabitas Hill west of the city, I think it was west, as a regular aiming point. Because nobody ever knew when artillery bombardment would begin, you could either find yourself running on the Gran Via or listening intently in Ilsa's room. Or at night, never with a flashlight, stumbling around new shell holes in the Gran Via. You took your copy to Ilsa who read it whenever she got around to it, and what happened afterwards I don't know. There wasn't any sense of haste. We all disliked Ilsa and were vilely smarmy with her. It was odd that they selected the upper floor of this bashed building as the center for their communications with the outside world.

The unattractive woman in Gellhorn's reminiscence was Ilsa Kulcsar, a thirty-something Austrian communist, not German communist. Dumpy, as Gellhorn says, and with a bad complexion. She spoke several languages and came after the failure of the Socialist uprising in Vienna in 1934. Daisy remembered her quite differently than Gellhorn. To Daisy, Ilsa was friendly and helpful. Ilsa Kulcsar believed that telling the truth would be better for the Republican cause than telling official lies that swept every defeat under the carpet and perpetuated the myth that the government was winning the war. Dos Passos shared Daisy's sympathy for Ilsa. "Only yesterday an Austrian woman came back to find that a shell fragment had set her room on fire and burned up all her shoes," he wrote for an American magazine.

Ilsa had been instrumental in talking Daisy out of going to Moscow to find Koltsov after he disappeared. Daisy's diary records the stormy session. "Ilsa is shaking me by the shoulder and saying, 'Don't you know what is going on in Moscow, you fool? Stalin's old comrades are being bumped off, as you say in America, one by one, and you are under suspicion. Oh, yes, you have been noticed. Your association with Mikhail has been noticed, and by very dangerous people indeed. You going to Moscow would certainly get Mikhail killed, and you, too, most probably, with a bullet in the nape of the neck. That's how they do it, you know. You kneel on the cement floor with the drain and they put a bullet in the nape of your neck. If you want my advice, go home! Leave Spain. Go back to America and forget all about this. You are one of the lucky ones with a home and a country to go back to. Get out while you still have the chance!'" But in the end, it was Ilsa and her cadaverous-looking boss and lover, Arturo Barea, who left Spain after having been fired from the censorship office. Daisy had warned Ilsa that the Gaylord Hotel Russians were whispering that Ilsa was a Trotskyite. Daisy gave Ilsa and her husband money to resettle in England in 1938.

I pause here to try to make sense of my mother's acts of charity in Spain, importing ambulances, bandaging the wounded, helping both Alvarez and Kulcsar escape and survive in exile. Can this be the same selfish woman who ran down her husband's mistress on a Long Island road in the summer of 1922 and never even stopped? Can this be the careless Daisy retreating into her wealth and expecting other people to clean up the mess, as Uncle Nick had described her?

Was her behavior in Spain just a way of belonging to the particular crowd to which she wanted to belong, just as superficial as had been her conversion to the avant garde in Paris in the twenties? Was she a war groupie grooving off the smell of cordite? Or was her time in Spain a kind of atonement for the two deaths on Long Island for which she had been directly and indirectly responsible?

By this time, Daisy was no longer in the first blossom of her youth. She was approaching forty. Her lustrous hair was showing strands of white. The scar on her forehead somewhat marred her ethereal beauty. She had also become very thin; I suspect with malnutrition. Her few letters to me never mentioned her living conditions. I had to get that from her diaries, which she never intended for me to see. I was in my later teens during the Spanish Civil War, and I wish to this day that she had taken me into her confidence.

"There were poppy petals in the new-dug trench, blown from the grass fields whipped flat from the wind from the snow-capped mountains," Hemingway wrote for his news agency. "Across the pine woods of the old royal hunting lodge rose the white skyline of Madrid. Forty yards away a light machine gun tapped in sharp deadliness and the bullets passed with the sick cracking sound that make recruits think they are explosive."

"I wonder what happened to the German who was the best man for night patrol in the Eleventh International Brigade?" wrote Martha Gellhorn. "He was a somber man, whose teeth were irregularly broken, whose fingertips were nailless pulp, the first graduate of Gestapo torture I had known."

These were dispatches that got passed by the censor, but others did not. Sometimes reporters used slang to get by the censor. When one wire service man discovered that the government was about to leave Madrid to set up shop in Valencia, he filed, "Bigwigs taking a powder," adding some nonsense about "in my dreams I hear you softly call to me." The censors knew that in the eighteenth-century wigs were powdered, but they could make nothing of the rest of it. The reporter's home office, however, knew that by quoting a line from the popular song *Valencia*, their reporter was telling them not just that the government was moving, but where. But, the government's move to Valencia made no difference to the day-to-day life in Madrid. The battle lines held. The war went on uninterrupted.

Dos and Hemingway had the satisfaction of getting their film made under harrowing war conditions. There was an apartment building along the Paseo Rosales on the outskirts of town which Hemingway and Herbert Matthews dubbed 'the Old Homestead'. From the comparative safety of the upper floors, they could watch and film battles unfolding before their eyes: men like ants swarming up a hill following tanks, beetle-like in the distance, and then the retreats when the assault wavered. One had to be careful lest the camera lens reflect the sunlight with a flash that would attract snipers from the Fascist side.

The Spanish Earth seems dated today, with noble peasants with worn faces working their fields, but it does show Spain as it was then. Alas, it made a limited impression in America. There was a private showing in the

White House, and it was shown in meeting halls and in anti-Fascist gatherings, but it was never released for wide distribution.

Many years later, I ran down the cameraman for the film, John Ferno, in Jerusalem, where he was living at the time. He told me that my mother had been fearless and obviously dedicated to the Republican cause, but totally uninterested in the infighting of Stalinists versus Trotskyites, Communists versus anarchists that so bedeviled the Loyalist side during the war. I also tried to interview the film's Dutch director, Joris Ivens, who was an ardent Communist and, by the time I got to him, an apologist for China's Chairman Mao. He shared Daisy's affection for Koltsov, whom he had known in Moscow before the Spanish war, but he was still angry at my mother for refusing to finance future films that Ivens was planning. "Your mother had plenty of money, and despite her efforts to seem otherwise, in her heart she remained always bourgeois," he told me in no uncertain terms. I got the impression that Ivens thought my mother should have been tried and shot for not financing him.

Daisy witnessed the friendship between Hemingway and Dos Passos end in bitterness and mutual recriminations. For twenty years, Dos had known a Spanish academic named Jose Robles, who became a professor of Spanish literature at Johns Hopkins University in America. He became a translator for Dos Passos's books into Spanish. Dark, good-looking, and exceedingly charming, he was well-liked by all who knew him. By coincidence, he was in Spain with his family on holiday when the war broke out in 1936 and decided to stay on to help the Republican cause.

In addition to English and French, Robles had learned Russian so he could read Russian literature in the original. Given the spy paranoia in Moscow at the time, it seems astonishing now that he was given a job in the Republic's war ministry as some sort of liaison officer with the Russians, but he was. Then he suddenly disappeared.

Hemingway took the position that if Robles had been arrested, he was probably guilty and would receive a fair trial. Dos Passos thought otherwise and became obsessed with trying to solve the mystery of his disappearance. Hemingway, and most of the Florida gang, thought Dos Passos was being overly sentimental. After all, the Republic was in a life-and-death struggle. Not so Daisy, who sided with Dos. "What is the point of friendship if you do nothing when your friend is lost?" she wrote. She mentioned the not-so-subtle letter that Uncle Nick had sent her describing how almost nobody showed up for Gatz's funeral. Of all the people who had supped at his table and drunk his wine through the long summer nights, none came. Of course, my father had forbidden her to go, but it gnawed at her now. And there was something in Hemingway's bullying of Dos that reminded her of Tom. The implication was that he, Hemingway, knew all about war, while Dos was clueless and gutless. This annoyed Daisy. Dos had been an ambulance driver in France during the First World War and had seen more of the horrors of war than Hemingway had in Italy.

The Republican counterespionage apparatus, the dreaded Commissariat of Investigation and Vigilance, was run by a pale, always impeccably dressed man named Pepe Quintanilla, known as the 'executioner of Madrid'.

Quintanilla was responsible for hundreds of summary executions on the Republican side. 'Thin lipped' is the description that pops up again and again, but Daisy thought he looked like a death's head with his dull, expressionless black eyes—the eyes of a sadist. Quintanilla was always flirting with pretty foreigners, like Daisy and Martha, and now Virginia Cowles, who was in Spain writing for Harper's Bazaar.

People often said that Ginny Cowles reminded them of Lauren Bacall, but Daisy thought her voice and her mannerisms reminded her more of Katharine Hepburn.

In order to find out what happened to Robles, Ginny Cowles and Daisy decided to lead Quintanilla on, perhaps to get him drunk, which he often was, in order to pump him for information. They thought if they went together, it would be safer, so they invited Quintanilla to dinner at the Gran Via Hotel. As hoped, he drank heavily. He invited them home for brandy at his apartment after the meal was over, and they accepted. But Daisy's notes say nothing of how that evening ended and nothing about what they may or may not have found out about the fate of Robles. I wrote to Cowles years later when she was living in London, and she replied that she felt lucky to have gotten out alive. She said she would come and see me, as she was planning a trip to France, but, alas, the meeting never took place. She died in a car crash while in France, and her story of what happened with Quintanilla died with her.

It was in the requisitioned palace of the Duke of Tovar, about a forty-minute drive from Madrid in the snow-topped Guadarrama Mountains, that Hemingway finally sank his sword between Dos's shoulder blades, in an act of profound cruelty. It took place during a celebration for the Eleventh International Brigade, which included the Abraham Lincolns. The Internationals were to be incorporated into the Spanish Army, and the ceremony was accompanied by a slightly off-key band, the kind one hears at provincial bullfights, playing the jaunty and lilting 'Hymn of Riego', the national anthem of the Republic. Following the ceremony there was a formal lunch in the duke's palace with portraits of the duke's ancestors staring down disapprovingly from the walls. Daisy thought that if these grandees were alive, they would all have been on Franco's side. During the lunch, Hemingway picked his moment to tell Dos what he had recently discovered: That Robles had been caught betraying the Republic to the Fascists, and that he had richly deserved the death sentence that he had received. Hemingway did not know how Robles had died, and Dos was not willing to let the matter rest.

In his rich imagination, Dos could picture how his friend had met his end, "The man stepping out to be court-martialed by his own side. The conversational tone of the proceedings. A joke or a smile that lets the blood flow easy again, but the gradual freezing recognition of the hundred ways a man may be guilty, the remark dropped in a cafe that someone wrote down, the letter you wrote last year, the sentence scribbled on a scratch pad, the fact that your cousin is in the ranks of the enemy, and the strange sound your own words make when they are quoted in the indictment. They shove a cigarette in your hand, and you walk out into the courtyard to face six men you have never seen before. They take aim. They wait for the order. They fire."

I found out from Daisy's diary that one of the Russians, a close friend of Koltsov's, had told her how Robles had died but that he had sworn her to secrecy lest she get Koltsov in trouble. Robles died in the damp cellar of the Russian embassy, half-dead already from the beatings, his linen soiled, with a bullet in the back of his head. It seems that Robles had gotten wind of a Russian plot to have the non-Communist militias in Barcelona, whom Moscow feared were led by anarchists and Trotskyites, eliminated. The anarchists were considered 'uncontrollable'.

The POUM, the Workers' Party of Marxist Unification, was to be suppressed, its leader murdered, and the government in Valencia brought down in favor of a more reliable government, a government more open to the Communists. Fearing that Robles might spill the beans, the Russians and their Spanish henchmen went to his apartment and dragged him out before his tearful wife could even pack a bag for him. These thugs found his diary, and although there was nothing especially incriminating in it, nor proof that he intended to show it to anybody, it was nonetheless forbidden to keep a diary of anything said or done in the defense ministry. Robles was taken straight to the Soviet embassy cellar for interrogation and death.

Daisy, despite her vow of silence to Koltsov, was tempted to tell Dos, but knowing how emotional he had become, she was afraid he would create a row endangering her lover. But she did seek to warn her friends in Barcelona, where Eric Blair had enlisted in the POUM militia, without mentioning how she knew. Both Eileen and Eric had been helpful to her in getting Señora Alvarez's relatives out of the country and getting her ambulances in. The city had been in the grip of a Red revolution far more radical than Madrid's, and it wasn't easy to deal with the anarchist dockworkers who decided when and how much they would work. They had to be persuaded that unloading ships was helping the revolution, and they would not accept any supervision. All bosses were enemies. It was said that not even the organ grinders' monkeys would obey their masters in Barcelona.

Eric Blair had been wounded on the front lines and was recovering when Eileen got through to him by telephone, warning him not to come home, that anyone connected with the POUM was about to be arrested. Blair spent his first night out of hospital in a church and the second in an open field. They left Spain as soon as they could on a ship bound for Marseilles, never to return. Eric would write his experiences up in a memoir, 'Homage to Catalonia', using his George Orwell pen name. It does not mention Daisy's warning, but it does chronicle his disillusionment with the Communists, who were taking too much control of the Spanish Republic.

As for Hemingway and Dos, in the end Daisy thought the real problem was that Dos hated and was revolted by the war, while Hemingway loved it. Certainly, Hemingway insisted he be considered the real expert on warfare, and he came to think of the Republic as right and noble. Dos, because of Robles, came to see the Republic as a tool of the Soviet Union. It made Daisy sad to see the bully Hemingway gaining control. A New York psychiatrist with the Lincoln Battalion, Bill Pike, explained Hemingway thus, "Generous, scrupulously honest and dedicated to his work, but lurking somewhere was a mean-spirited, uncertain, frightened, aggressive child."

Back in America, Gerald Murphy tried to patch up the quarrel between the two old friends. He arranged a meeting in his apartment with Dos and Ernest when they returned from Spain. "I tried my absolute best," Murphy told me when I went to see him in his house on the Hudson. "I really tried, and I thought I had succeeded. I said to them, 'I keep my friends as misers do their treasure because, of all the things granted to us by wisdom, none is greater or better than friendship'." But with that Murphy stared into the distance and fell silent. And Dos remained bitter the rest of his life. His politics swung more and more to the right, and the last time I saw him, more than fifty years ago, he was working on the campaign of Barry Goldwater for president of the United States. He remembered Daisy fondly. "We all loved your mother," he told me. "She was a little naive politically, and like me back then she had swallowed the propaganda of the left. But she had an upbeat personality that cheered us up in those difficult days, and that lovely voice of hers made us feel she loved us too." By that time Hemingway was dead by his own hand. Dos lived on, but his talent died in Spain.

The betrayal of Czechoslovakia by Britain and France in the autumn of 1938 convinced Stalin of what he had long suspected: that he was on his own as far as resistance to Nazi Germany was concerned. And because Russia was in no way ready for war, he played for time and started actively planning to make a pact with Hitler. Subsequently, Russian support for the Spanish Republic began to dry up, and both France and Britain started to talk about recognizing the Nationalist regime which appeared to be winning the war. Germany, Italy, and the Vatican had already done so…

Late in 1938, the International Brigades were withdrawn from Spain by orders from the Republican government in the forlorn hope that if they got rid of their foreigners, international pressure would pry Germany and Italy from intervening in the Spanish war. Daisy was thrilled upon hearing La Pasionaria's farewell to the departing international volunteers. "They gave up everything, their homes, their country and fortune… they came and told us, 'We are here, your cause, Spain's cause is ours…' Today they are going away. Many of them, thousands of them, are staying here with the Spanish earth for their shroud…" Did Daisy see something of herself in those international volunteers? They marched their last march down Barcelona's broad Diagonal Avenue, their bedrolls over their shoulders, often out of step and up to their ankles in flowers, while thousands of Catalans cheered them.

As 1938 drifted into 1939, General Franco's forces slowly and relentlessly advanced across Spain with only the occasional reversal. Daisy's gang at the Florida had long since begun to drift away to other stories as Europe teetered toward world war. The Russians at the Gaylord began packing up for their departure, leaving another gap in Daisy's life. She seems to have believed that against all odds, the French, the British, and maybe the Americans would see the light and come in on the Republic's side before it was too late. She didn't know that the British Prime Minister, Stanley Baldwin, had said it was a good thing to have a place like Spain, where the Fascists and the Communists could kill each other off.

Madrid was becoming a lonely place for her, but she kept up her work helping with the wounded. Once in a while she would drop by Chicote's, but with the correspondents gone, Chicote's had a sense of the morning after about it. There was so little fuel that when the cold weather came, people began breaking up their furniture to burn. Food was in such short supply that the population lived on a ration of lentils, beans, and occasionally salt cod. Starvation was beginning to show its ugly face in the city. The last horse and the last mule within the city limits had long since been consumed. Even the fighting bulls had been eaten, and before long cats, dogs, and pigeons found themselves stalked in the city's parks in that last terrible winter of the war. As she had one last vodka with the departing Russians she feared for them, as well she might. Many of them were arrested and shot or sent to the gulags, victims of Stalin's paranoia.

The Republic was entering its death agonies when an obscure colonel named Segismundo Casado, an officer in the old prewar army who had remained loyal to the Republic, decided it was time to stop the war. He thought that by purging the Communists he could make a deal with Franco. The Republic still controlled a large part of Spain. The loyalists still had bargaining power, Casado thought. He was wrong, of course; Franco wanted nothing less than unconditional surrender and re-imposition of the old church-based, semi-feudal order with himself as dictator.

But the ever-hopeful Casado, whom Daisy referred to as 'silly Segi', declared a coup d'etat and set up a National

Defense Junta. What was left of the official government, including La Pasionaria, fled into exile and spent the rest of their lives quarreling among themselves over who lost Spain. The junta began rounding up and imprisoning Communists, and in early March, army units loyal to Casado began to fight it out with the Communists in the streets of Madrid. Daisy stayed indoors at the Florida while bullets flew outside, one or two coming through her window. She wrote that she was more afraid of the anarchy at her door than she had been under Franco's artillery. The Fascist forces simply waited outside while their enemies tore at each other's throats inside the doomed city.

Daisy was not optimistic about Casado's chances for a negotiated peace, nor did she have many doubts about what Franco had in mind for those who had remained loyal to the Republic. Franco had announced that support for the Republic was a criminal act and that you could be deemed guilty even for the sin of 'vexatious passivity', which could be nothing more than not helping the Fascists. Casado's forces prevailed, but Franco wasn't buying, and it became clear to Daisy that she had better leave the capital soon. She contacted an air force pilot she had met at Chicote's, who promised, for a great deal of money, to take her along as he made his escape to Oran in Algeria the following morning. She showed up at the Barajas airdrome just before dawn on the appointed day, only to find that the pilot had taken her money and left without her.

At that time, Daisy had a desperate feeling that her world was closing down upon her. Austria had been erased to become part of the Third Reich, Czechoslovakia had been betrayed, and Barcelona had fallen to the Fascists. Britain and France had switched diplomatic recognition to Franco's side. The shipments of medical supplies she had bought and paid for were not arriving anymore in Valencia as scheduled. On the twenty-sixth of March, soldiers, as soldiers always long to do, started drifting away from their trenches to go home. Their officers did nothing to prevent them, and the roads were crowded with the disintegrating army of the Republic. There were several suicides, one of a Republican general whom Daisy had known well, right outside on the Gran Via on the Republic's last morning. In the Casa de Campo, Daisy saw soldiers on both sides embracing each other, and at eleven in the morning of the twenty-eighth the defenders of Madrid, who had held out for two and a half years, offered their surrender in the university's bullet-pocked Clinical Hospital. "Convenient for the Republic to die in hospital," Daisy noted with bitterness. Pope Pius XII wired the victorious Francisco Franco saying, "Lifting up our hearts to God, we give sincere thanks with your Excellency for Spain's Catholic victory." The war was over.

Daisy was out in the streets when hundreds of Franco sympathizers, the dreaded fifth column, emerged from foreign embassies and from cellars, where they had hidden for two and a half years; pale-faced and blinking in the sunlight. Daisy was astonished at their numbers. Nationalist soldiers quickly and efficiently took over government buildings, and cheering crowds threw flowers at the feet of the conquering army, crying out, "Franco, Franco, Franco" and "Han Pasado!" They have passed. The red and yellow flag of the old Spain broke out from windows and balconies, the red, yellow, and purple flag of the Republic banished forever.

On the first of April, the United States formally recognized the new Nationalist government of Spain, which appalled Daisy, but she did make a note that it might make it easier for her to leave Spain in an orderly manner once things had settled down. She wrote that she could not contemplate staying in the new Fascist Spain a day longer than she had to. "Thank God I have my American passport," she wrote. "Goodbye, Spain." And there Daisy's diary ends. What happened to her after the first of April 1939, I was not to know for thirty years.

j

My mother was an infrequent correspondent, so I was not alarmed at first that I hadn't heard from her for a long while. I was not yet twenty when the Spanish War ended, and with my father dead and my mother missing, I was on my own. When it looked as if the war in Europe was about to begin, Uncle Nick suggested that I come back to the States. But since my mother was presumably still alive—at least there had been no reports of her death—I had no official guardian, and I begged to stay on to continue my education in neutral Switzerland. The war in Europe began that September, and still no word of my mother. Spain was neutral, and Uncle Nick asked the State Department to inquire about Daisy. Our ambassador in Madrid at the time, Alexander Weddell, was new to the job, but he tried his best. He came up with nothing.

Coming into my maturity, I could do pretty much what I liked, so I continued my education in England and then France. By 1946, my mother had been missing for seven years, and there was some discussion of declaring her legally dead. Since I was her only heir, I became involved. It was then that I started my quest to find her. I went to Madrid but ran into nothing but stone walls. "You must realize, madame, that this was a very confused time. We had just taken the reins of government from the Reds, and it was some time before law and order could be restored. You say your mother was involved in supplying the previous government with medical supplies? Was she involved politically? No? If it was just humanitarian aid, she might have stayed on to help the Spanish people. We were short of medical supplies in 1939. If not, why didn't she ask to be repatriated immediately upon our victory? We have always tried to maintain good relations with your esteemed country, madame. Perhaps your embassy could be of some assistance?" I was waiting for them to accuse my mother of vexatious inaction. It was a chilling time. I learned that the Nationalist army had rolled into Madrid on the first day the city fell, full of documents to begin prosecuting the losers. The firing squads were seldom silent during those first years of Franco's reign, with hundreds being executed every day.

After finding nothing in Spain, I turned my attention to the refugee communities in France and in Mexico, where many Spanish Republicans had settled. I spread a lot of money around and got some very spurious information, as you can imagine, but one contact seemed promising. It was a woman who claimed to have walked with Daisy trying to get across the French frontier in those last days of the war.

You must remember that I had not then recovered Daisy's diaries, so I had no idea that she had remained in Madrid until the end. The woman gave an accurate description of Daisy and seemed to have facts about her that confirmed her knowledge. The woman said that Daisy had died of typhus fever in the town of Figueres before they could get across the border. She had been sick for some time and simply could not go on. The woman said that my mother's last words were of me, which was of course what I wanted to hear at the time. But under further questioning my doubts rose.

Spain's relationship with the United States improved in the fifties when we started basing our bombers there for the Cold War, and it seemed that Franco had assumed in our American eyes the role he always wanted to play: Defender of Western civilization against the Red hordes. As previously mentioned, I recovered Daisy's diaries in the sixties, when the Florida was about to be torn down, but my real breakthrough came after Franco's death in 1975, when a period of liberalization began. Old, buried stories of the war years emerged. The fate of the poet Federico Garcia Lorca was a big concern at the time, and I hired a historian to delve through the available records to find word of my mother, which he did.

The records showed that Daisy had been denounced to the Nationalist authorities in the spring of 1939 by a Spanish exile with connections to Franco's representative in Britain at the time, the Duke of Alba. The woman—for it was a woman—claimed to have known Daisy before and during the Spanish Civil War. She had, in fact, taught Daisy

Spanish. The woman claimed that Daisy had dangerous political views.

It was the association with Koltsov that sealed her fate. Witnesses were found who knew of their companionship— servants at the Gaylord. Evidence was produced that indicated she might have been a spy. The allegation was enough. No proof needed. She was executed on the eighteenth of May, 1939, the day before Franco's big victory parade, just weeks before her fortieth birthday. I can only imagine her end. They didn't offer her a last cigarette the way Dos Passos had imagined the execution of his friend, Robles. To save time, several condemned persons were often executed at once. They were in a hurry in those days. So many people to be killed. Trials were short and perfunctory. Sometimes a machine gun would be used instead of a firing squad. More efficient.

In my imagination, I see six or seven women being led out into the prison courtyard. They are lined up against a brick wall. A truck is backed up in front of them. Daisy thinks for a fleeting moment of that time driving home from the Plaza in New York when a woman rushed out in the road, and the sickening sound as the car strikes her. Suddenly the back of the truck flops open, and a machine gun is revealed. One man at the trigger. Another to feed the rounds. They await the order. The women reach for each other's hands.

The End